THE **BEES** OF NORFOLK

Nick Owens

piscespublications

For Frankie

Published 2017 by Pisces Publications

First published 2017.

British-Library-in-Publication Data
A catalogue record for this book is available from the British Library.

ISBN 978-1-874357-78-0

Designed and published by Pisces Publications

Visit our bookshop
www.naturebureau.co.uk/bookshop/

Pisces Publications is the imprint of NatureBureau,
36 Kingfisher Court, Hambridge Road, Newbury, Berkshire RG14 5SJ
www.naturebureau.co.uk

Printed and bound by Gomer Press, UK

MIX
Paper from
responsible sources
FSC® C114687

Front cover   Large Scabious Mining Bee *Andrena hattorfiana* [PC]
Back cover   Heather Colletes *Colletes succinctus*

Contents

Acknowledgements

This book is based on the ground work of generations of naturalists, starting with those who first gave scientific names to bees in the 18th century. I picked up the bee bug about seven years ago with an ambition to get to know all our local species, to photograph them and to understand something about their behaviour.

First I must mention Tim Strudwick who with great patience identified hundreds of bee images and gave detailed advice about how to recognise them. He has been most generous with his time as well as providing validated records from the county database which are the basis of the distribution maps.

I have enjoyed many profitable hours in the field in the company of like-minded people, including David Baldock, Ted Benton, Andy Bloomfield, David Bratt, Paul Brock, Dorothy Cheyne, Andy Clarke, Rob Coleman, Rosie Earwaker, George Else, Francis Farrow, John Furse, Ramón and Miguel Gomez de la Cuesta, Martin Greenland, Ian Keymer, Ash Murray, Richard Porter, Nigel Robson, Moss Taylor, Roger Tidman, John Wagstaff and Mark Webster. My thanks too to the landowners who gave permission to enter their sites.

Tony Irwin has been of great help at Norwich Castle Museum as well as with identifications. I have also been assisted at Cambridge by Ed Turner and Russell Stebbings and at the Natural History Museum by David Notton.

Members of the Bees, Wasps and Ants Recording Society have been very supportive of my endeavours and little progress would have been made without the use of draft keys produced by George Else for his forthcoming book, with Mike Edwards, on the Bees of the British Isles. Both have also dealt with many identification challenges. Steven Falk has also kindly provided feedback to a large number of questions.

Information about bees in other counties was supplied by Michael Archer, Peter Harvey, Adrian Knowles and Alan Phillips.

Lizzy Oddy at Norfolk Biodiversity Information Service provided data on land use while Ed Cross gave useful advice about conservation and farming and Alec Bull provided insights about brambles. Pete Murray gave essential advice about cameras and many photographers have generously supplied additional images for the book. Photographers are credited on p.210.

To be especially thanked are all those who have contributed Norfolk bee records over the years, many of them members of the Norfolk and Norwich Naturalists' Society. This society has played a large part in providing inspiration and support for this book. Peter Creed, Creative Director of NatureBureau, has done much inventive design and patient work in transforming my rough drafts into the finished book. He has also provided a number of excellent images including the front cover.

Lastly I must thank my family for putting up with a bee botherer in their midst.

Nick Owens

Introduction

Bees are to be found during the really fine weather of spring, summer and autumn, when the country is in its loveliest state; and the situations it takes one to are the most attractive, where the wild flowers bloom the most freely; can anything be more delightful than to find one's self in such a place, the air laden with the perfume of many flowers, and alive with these industrious little creatures?

[John B Bridgman, Presidential Address to the Norfolk and Norwich Naturalists' Society, 28 March 1876]

Most people are familiar with Honeybees and bumblebees but few realise how many other bees there are. There are over 270 species of bees recorded in the British Isles with 197 so far recorded in Norfolk. This project started in 2009 when my interests expanded from bumblebees to embrace the other aculeates, the group that comprises all the ants bees and wasps. The number of small bees to be found was something of a revelation and I soon realised that I had been overlooking many species in my own garden. Most of these are solitary bees, meaning that each female makes its own nest, gathers pollen and lays eggs without the help of any worker bees. But some small bees are social in a comparable way to bumblebees.

The book is intended as an introduction to identifying Norfolk's bees but is not a comprehensive identification guide. Steven Falk's *Field Guide to the Bees of Great Britain and Ireland* already fulfils this purpose very well. After some thought I decided to use just the scientific names for bees in the text. Falk's suggested common names are given in the species accounts and are also listed in the index. The only common names

used are Honeybee and bumblebee. Capitals are used for bee species names such as Honeybee or Buff-tailed Bumblebee and lower case for general names such as bumblebee. For plants, common names in lower case are used throughout as these are well established. Plant names conform to those in Stace's *New Flora of the British Isles,* 3rd Edition.

This book aims to shine a spotlight on the county's bees, showing how diverse and beautiful they are and how their populations are faring. It is hoped that it will help readers new to bees to be able to recognise many of the species they are looking at and encourage them to learn more. For more experienced bee watchers it will provide a source of reference about Norfolk's bees and a baseline on which to build further knowledge. It is the culmination of seven years looking at bees in Norfolk and beyond, recording localities, dates, flowers visited and nest sites. I have attempted to photograph all the Norfolk species, and have managed to obtain images of the majority. Images of many of the missing species were kindly provided by others.

The first challenge was learning to identify bees. This could not have happened without the support of experts who have provided keys and assisted with identifying photographs and specimens. The other major task has been to assimilate the records for each species and produce distribution maps, again building on the foundations of a small number of like-minded people in the county. This is not the last word on the county's bees, it is simply an update on the work started by a long line of county naturalists. It also includes an introduction to bee behaviour and ecology in the hope that this will encourage people to look beyond identification and to start observing bees in the wild and be able to contribute further to our knowledge.

The state of Norfolk's bees

Between the earliest records in the 19th century to the present day, 197 bee species have been recorded in the county out of a total of 276 bee species recorded in the British Isles as a whole. Nine of the 276 species have been seen only in the Channel Isles and 12 further species are known from just one or two old records on the mainland. This gives a total of about 255 bee species well established on the British mainland at some time during the past 200 years or so. Some examples of other county bee totals (including historical records) produced this century are shown (left) in rank order. Despite differences in recording effort and county size, there is a clear trend for there to be less bee diversity in more northerly counties, a pattern seen in many insect groups.

Cumbria	119
Worcestershire	138
Lincolnshire	141
Staffordshire	143
Warwickshire	143
Yorkshire	144
Shropshire	155
Cornwall	180
Norfolk	**197**
Suffolk	207
Essex	207
Kent	217
Dorset	220
Surrey	222

LOSSES

Twenty-three bee species once present in the county have been unrecorded for many years and may be extinct in Norfolk. Some of these, shown in brackets, have only one county record. Thirteen of the 23 lost species have not been seen since the 19th century: *Andrena labialis*, *A. niveata*, (*A. proxima*), (*A. simillima*), *A. tridentata*, *Eucera longicornis*, *Coelioxys quadridentata*, (*Hylaeus pictipes*), (*Osmia pilicornis*), *Nomada obtusifrons*, *N. sexfasciata*, (*Sphecodes ferruginatus*) and *S. rubicundus*. Nine species have not been seen since the 1960s or earlier in the 20th century: *Anthophora retusa*, *Bombus distinguendus*, *B. humilis*, *B. subterraneus*, *B. sylvarum*, (*Lasioglossum xanthopus*), (*L. zonulum*), *Nomada armata* and *N. roberjeotiana*. One species has been lost between 1970 and 2000: (*N. integra*). Two of the lost species, *A. tridentata* and *B. subterraneus*, are thought to have become extinct in the British Isles as a whole, though the latter species is now the subject of a reintroduction programme. It is quite possible that some of the above species are still present in Norfolk but overlooked. Five long-lost Norfolk species have been rediscovered in the past eight years: *Andrena angustior*, *A. argentata*, *A. minutuloides*, *A. trimmerana* and *A. varians*.

GAINS

Seventeen bee species have been recorded for the first time in the county since around the year 2000.

Six of these are rare and may have been present for a long time but not noticed: *Andrena lapponica*, *Lasioglossum pauperatum*, *L. puncticolle*, *Nomada baccata*, *Sphecodes spinulosus* and *Stelis ornatula*, while ten species have almost certainly spread into the county: *Andrena cineraria*, *A. flavipes*, *Bombus hypnorum*, *Colletes hederae*, *C. cunicularius*, *Heriades truncorum*, *Melitta tricincta*, *Nomada fucata*, *N. lathburiana* and *Panurgus calcaratus*. In addition *B. monticola* has been recorded as a vagrant.

	All records	Lost pre-2000	Gains post-2000	Post 2000	British Isles (not Ch I)
Andrena	47	5	3	42	68
Anthidium	1			1	1
Anthophora	5	1		4	5
Apis	1			1	1
Bombus	22	4	2	18	24
Ceratina	0			0	1
Chelostoma	2			2	2
Coelioxys	5	1		4	6
Colletes	8		2	8	9
Dasypoda	1			1	1
Dufourea	0			0	2
Epeolus	2			2	2
Eucera	1	1		0	2
Halictus	3			3	6
Heriades	1		1	1	1
Hoplitis	1			1	2
Hylaeus	9	1		8	12
Lasioglossum	25	2	2	23	33
Macropis	1			1	1
Megachile	7			7	7
Melecta	1			1	1
Melitta	3		1	3	4
Nomada	24	5	3	19	29
Osmia	7	1		6	12
Panurgus	2		1	2	2
Sphecodes	15	2	1	13	16
Stelis	3		1	3	4
Xylocopa	0			0	1
	197	23	17	174	255

CAUSES OF POPULATION CHANGE

Large species Large bee species are likely to require larger foraging areas than smaller species and therefore be more vulnerable to habitat degradation and fragmentation. Four bumblebee species have been lost from the county. *Bombus distinguendus*, *B. humilis*, *B. subterraneus* and *B. sylvarum* emerge late from hibernation and specialise in flower-rich grasslands; habitats which have largely gone. Other bumblebee species survive only along the coast, such as *B. muscorum*, or apparently have a higher density in coastal areas, such as *B. jonellus*, *B. lapidarius* and several others. The coastline of Norfolk remains well protected for much of its length and probably offers more food resources than many inland areas, though the impression may be exaggerated by having more recording from coastal areas. Bumblebees are particularly vulnerable because each nest contains just one breeding bee (the queen) and the nest requires a large foraging area. Other large bee species have been lost including *Eucera longicornis* and *Anthophora retusa*. *Anthidium manicatum* seems to have declined considerably.

Specialised species Bees may be threatened through being specialised in their choice of habitat or pollen source. *Andrena hattorfiana* and *A. marginata* take pollen almost exclusively from scabious, and are found only where these plants flourish. At Earlham Cemetery a population of *A. hattorfiana* survives which has probably persisted since the cemetery was bordered by open fields. This kind of isolation may lead to inbreeding depression in the longer term.

Climate change Several of the new arrivals to Norfolk have spread across the county in just a few years, showing that there is still enough suitable habitat for less specialised species and sufficient connectivity for bees to spread to new sites. It is likely that bees are better able to tolerate more marginal habitats as the climate becomes milder, allowing more days of activity, especially in the spring and autumn. Seven out of the ten bee species which have spread into the county since the year 2000 use tree pollen. Trees and shrubs have declined less than grassland flowers and continue to offer a lot of spring pollen in the county, especially willows which have increased in some areas as gravel pits have become worked out. *Colletes hederae* is an exception in being an autumn bee which uses Ivy pollen. Two of the gains, *Heriades truncorum* and *Panurgus calcaratus* use yellow Asteraceae pollen in grasslands and these may also be more available with increased temperatures which allow their flowers to open for longer hours. So far these two are confined to the Brecks.

Melitta tricincta was first recorded in the Brecks in 2009 and has now spread as far as Flitcham. Its only pollen source is red bartsia. This is an annual plant which flourishes in field margins and gateways often in compacted ground, so the bee does not necessarily need flower-rich permanent grassland. Red bartsia has long been widespread in Norfolk and it seems likely that the spread of *M. tricincta* is a response to the warming climate.

We can expect bee species to differ in their responses to climate warming. The table (right) shows the total number of *Andrena*, *Lasioglossum* and *Bombus* species recorded from six eastern coastal counties. In *Andrena* the effects of latitude are dramatic with species almost halving between Kent and Yorkshire. *Lasioglossum* species reduce by about one-third while *Bombus* show little or no change. Bees can be active only when their body temperatures rise beyond a critical level. *Bombus* can generate their own body heat and can remain active down to almost freezing point. On this evidence we might expect *Andrena* species to advance more rapidly with climate warming than *Lasioglossum* or *Bombus*. It should be added that there are some bees with northerly distributions: *Lasioglossum rufitarse* occurs in Yorkshire and Lincolnshire but not in the four more southerly counties listed.

A warming climate can change the balance between closely related species. Chris Plowright suggests that *Bombus pascuorum* is gradually supplanting *B. muscorum* in Norfolk and elsewhere, perhaps because *B. pascuorum* is less resistant to cold wet conditions than *B. muscorum*, and is able to compete better as the climate warms.

Dispersal We know very little about how and when bees disperse, how far they can travel or what makes them decide to go. The first *Colletes hederae* females at Weybourne in 2014 were very large and seemingly not accompanied by males: it may be that it is mated female bees that disperse soon after emerging and perhaps the larger individuals. Queen bumblebees can be observed flying along the Norfolk coast in spring and autumn, perhaps part of general multi-directional dispersal which is diverted along the beach.

We are now very familiar with the Tree Bumblebee *Bombus hypnorum* which was first seen in Norfolk in 2008 and spread across the county within three years. This bumblebee still appears not to have a cuckoo bumblebee attacking it, and has already reached Scotland. It has a short tongue and uses a very wide range of flower species. Its preference for nesting above ground has allowed it to set up home under tiles and in bird nest boxes across the county.

Andrena (A), *Lasioglossum* (L) and *Bombus* (B) species recorded in east coast counties

	A	L	B
Yorkshire	32	16	22
Lincolnshire	34	18	21
Norfolk	47	25	22
Suffolk	53	27	22
Essex	53	26	19
Kent	58	25	24

Urban spread J B Bridgman describes a nesting aggregation of *Eucera longicornis* at Postwick near Norwich in the 1870s, when the colony extended to a quarter of a mile, attended by its cleptoparasite *Nomada sexfasciata*. Unsurprisingly these bees do not survive at the Postwick Hub (a new road interchange) today. However, the spread of the city is not necessarily bad. The rare *Anthophora quadrimaculata* has recently been rediscovered in west Norwich gardens where it frequents catmint and lavender. Gardens, green spaces, allotments and even roundabouts can support a good range of bees if sympathetically managed. Business parks often have untended corners free from sprays where bees can be found. Brownfield sites can be excellent, having warm microclimates, bare ground and a range of native and garden plants. The fields adjacent to towns and villages are often small and less intensively farmed and can offer good bee habitat.

Missing bees There are a few species that might be expected to be present in Norfolk but are not. *Osmia aurulenta* has one doubtful record in the county and is not otherwise present north of the Thames Valley. The habitat is suitable for it and its range extends up to Dumfriesshire on the west coast. *Coelioxys mandibularis* is a cleptoparasite of *Megachile leachella* in south Wales and in Kent but has not been recorded in Norfolk despite a strong population of its host.

Coming soon? A few species are advancing northwards and may reach Norfolk soon. These include *Andrena florea*, *A. vaga*, *Ceratina cyanea*, *Eucera longicornis* (returning) and perhaps *Stelis breviuscula* whose host, *Heriades truncorum*, has recently arrived in the county.

Andrena florea on white bryony Le Crotoy, France June. This species is advancing slowly northwards and was first seen in Suffolk in 2015. It specialises on white bryony pollen

Andrena vaga and its cleptoparasite *Nomada lathburiana*, Le Crotoy, France April. This bee re-colonised the south coast from about 2009 and reached Essex in 2016

Bee habitats in Norfolk

BRECKLAND

The low rainfall and light sandy soils of this area provide favourable habitats for species which are sensitive to cold, wet conditions. The Brecks still contain good areas of flower-rich grassland including the Stanford Training Area and miles of forest rides, as well as heather rich heathland. It is often the area first colonised by bee species expanding their range into the county, for example *Colletes cunicularius*, *Panurgus calcaratus* and *Heriades truncorum*, which were first recorded in Norfolk post-2000 in the Brecks. Other Norfolk species with a large proportion of their records in the Brecks, though not all found exclusively here, include *Anthophora bimaculata*, *Coelioxys conoidea*, *Dasypoda hirtipes*, *Halictus confusus*, *Hoplitis claviventris*, *Lasioglossum brevicorne*, *L. prasinum*, *L. sexnotatum*, *Megachile maritima*, *Nomada flavopicta*, *N. sheppardana*, *N. signata*, *Osmia bicolor* and *Stelis ornatula*. For *Colletes marginatus*, Breckland is the only significant inland site in the British Isles, perhaps partly because of the presence of good amounts of wild mignonette, an important food source. Similarly, Breckland provides a good source of harebells for *Melitta haemorrhoidalis* whose centre of population is in the Brecks.

WOODLAND

Woodlands, woodland edges and tree lined fields provide habitats for many bee species with 57 species recorded at Swanton Novers Woods for example. Floriferous woodland rides and glades provide sheltered habitats with major sources of food for spring bees in the form of bluebells, ground-ivy, bugle, clovers, yellow archangel and a variety of others. Many of these have deep corollas and attract long-tongued species. Here can be found many bumblebee queens and their cuckoos, *Andrena* bees and associated *Nomada*

Beech root plate occupied by a nest aggregation of *Lasioglossum parvulum*, Sheringham Park

Breckland grassland [TC]

species, *Osmia bicornis*, *Megachile versicolor* and *Anthophora plumipes*. *Andrena fucata* has been recorded largely in wooded heathland or woodland rides while *A. helvola* appears to be more closely associated with established woodland. Wild raspberry, bird cherry, holly and sycamore are important woodland food sources whilst honeysuckle is accessible to the long-tongued *Bombus hortorum*. Woodland nest sites include hollow stems as well as bare ground on wood banks and root plates. The early spring bee *Andrena clarkella* nests in aggregations in root plates well within the woodland canopy and completes its activity before the leaves fully emerge. Glades and rides in coniferous woodland can be rich in foxgloves, also much used by *Bombus hortorum*. Many of our common bumblebees are woodland edge specialists and find leafy gardens to their liking.

HEATHLAND

A large proportion of Norfolk's bee species occur on heathland (69 species on Kelling Heath including 21 *Andrena* species) because it offers a warm microclimate with bare sandy areas and small cliffs for nesting. Common gorse and western gorse between them provide flowers throughout much of the season while bell heather flowers from June and heather (ling) from July. Wood sage, bramble and yellow Asteraceae such

as cat's-ear provide major pollen sources from mid-summer and are used by several *Lasioglossum* species and by *Panurgus banksianus*. *Andrena fuscipes* is dependent on heather (ling) pollen and its cleptoparasite *Nomada rufipes* shares its habitat. *Colletes succinctus* and its cleptoparasite *Epeolus cruciger* are also strongly associated with heather (ling). *Bombus jonellus* occurs on several heaths where it uses gorse in the spring and heathers later on, though it is not confined to heathland. On heathland margins there is often a transition from heathland to scrub and woodland, widening the range of habitats. Norfolk County Council has played an active role in re-establishing good heathland management since the 1990s.

CHALK GRASSLAND

This is a scarce habitat in Norfolk since most chalky land is used for arable cultivation, except in the Brecks. The western half of the county, excluding the Fens and the Greensand heaths, has most of the calcareous habitats, though pockets of chalky soils occur over a wide area and the boulder clays in the south of the county are chalky. Archaeological sites which have escaped the plough such as Castle Acre, Grimes Graves and Warham Camp are good chalk sites. There is also sandy chalk along the banks of the Cut-off Channel notably at Stoke Ferry where bare ground supports a wide range of aculeates. At a site near Flitcham, 15 hectares of chalk grassland have been re-established since 1994 using a diverse range of seeds collected from local sites. This approach, funded by Natural England's Stewardship schemes, has been followed by land managers on several other sites in north Norfolk, with more projects planned. Fifty-four bee species have so far been recorded at Flitcham including three *Melitta* species. *Andrena hattorfiana* and *A. marginata* both have strong populations here. These species show an association with chalk because they are dependent on scabious as a source of pollen,

Kelling Heath in April with gorse and blackthorn, and in August with heather (ling), bell heather and western gorse

Small scabious and other chalkland flowers [CW]

though field scabious occurs on other light soils too. *Osmia bicolor* is associated with calcareous habitats owing to its use of empty snail shells as a nest site and is spreading out from the Brecks. Other Norfolk species seemingly associated with calcareous places are *Andrena alfkenella*, *Lasioglossum fulvicorne* and its cleptoparasite *Sphecodes hyalinatus* and *S. spinulosus* and its host, *L. xanthopus* but the reasons for their preference for this habitat are not yet clear. The well-draining, quickly warming soils may be advantageous for nesting and this may be just as important as the plant species present.

SCRUB, VERGES AND HEDGEROWS
Many spring *Andrena*, *Nomada*, *Osmia* and queen *Bombus* species are highly dependent on flowering shrubs, especially willows, cherry plum, blackthorn, crab apple, alder buckthorn, dogwood and hawthorn. Alexanders also provides a source of nectar and pollen to many species from early spring until May, especially near the coast. Later in the season, bramble, hogweed, yellow Asteraceae and white bryony attract many species. Hedges and other boundaries are also used by swarming or patrolling male bees seeking mates, which can be seen pausing to scent mark on stems and leaves. Hedgerows tend to be richer in plant species in the east and south of the county where field enclosures were earlier and more irregular, in contrast to the more recently enclosed land in the west which gave rise to large regular shaped fields with species poor hedges. Scrub is a scarce habitat in the county but can be very rich in bees in the early stages of succession.

BROWNFIELD SITES AND WASTE PLACES
Abandoned land often makes very good bee habitat, usually comprising a mixture of native and naturalised plant species and benefitting from a lack of sprays. The topography is often uneven providing microhabitats and nesting sites. Such sites are very vulnerable to development or inappropriate tidying up and tree planting. *Bombus ruderarius* is still present at the Thorpe St Andrew hospital site in Norwich. A site at Bowthorpe has produced *Andrena pilipes* while the area of Caistor St Edmund chalk pit has produced *A. barbilabris*, *A. humilis*, *A. thoracica*, *Lasioglossum pauperatum*, *L. quadrinotatum*, *Nomada ferruginata*, *N. sheppardana*, *Sphecodes crassus*, *S. longulus*, *S. miniatus* and *S. niger*.

GARDENS
Gardens managed sympathetically for bees can attract a wide range of species and the

The author's garden and workshop

Cottage garden flowers for bees

author's small garden in Weybourne, which backs on to farmland, has so far produced 63 species, including 15 species of bumblebee. Tim Strudwick's garden at Brundall has attracted 65 species (see p.204). *Anthophora plumipes* can be seen in the majority of gardens in early spring, while *A. furcata* occurs in some and the rare *A. quadrimaculata* has recently been re-discovered in a Norwich garden. This species and *Anthidium manicatum* take nectar from garden catmint. *Anthidium* uses hairs from the leaves of lamb's-ear to make its nest and its rare cleptoparasite *Stelis punctulatissima* also occurs in some gardens. Several *Osmia* species are easily found, especially if artificial tube nest sites are provided. *O. bicornis* is often the first to occupy these, but *O. leaiana* and *O. caerulescens* are often also present. *Megachile* species will come to knapweeds and thistles and will nest in wider hollow stems, especially *M. centuncularis*, *M. willughbiella* and *M. ligniseca*. Their *Coelioxys* cleptoparasites require careful searching but appear periodically at many artificial nest sites.

CHURCHYARDS AND CEMETERIES
Norfolk has the highest number of churchyards of any county and these often preserve remnants of the flower rich grasslands that were once

a while even though the daffodils themselves are of little value. Lesser celandines are attractive to Honeybees, *Andrena* and *Nomada* species especially. Many churchyards contain ground-ivy which attracts *Anthophora plumipes* and its cleptoparasite *Melecta albifrons* in early spring. As mentioned, Earlham Cemetery in Norwich hosts a population of *Andrena hattorfiana* and the site is managed sympathetically for this species through the encouragement of field scabious. Rosary Cemetery in the city also has a diverse bee fauna including *A. helvola*. Some country churchyards including Blofield and Saxlingham Nethergate support *Andrena labiata*, which favours germander speedwell. Many contain a good range of *Lasioglossum* species including *L. smeathmanellum*. Ivy also provides an important food source.

THE COAST

Many bee species use the soft cliffs between Weybourne and Happisburgh as nest sites, the most attractive locations being those with promontories receiving the morning sun. The cliffs are often backed by unimproved grassland, some of it established in recent years through agri-environment schemes. Established dunes are very attractive to bees, offering abundant nest sites, quickly warming ground and good pollen sources in the form of Asteraceae, Fabaceae, sea holly, thrift, sea-lavender and bramble, though

widespread. The Norfolk Wildlife Trust has run the Norfolk Churchyard Conservation Scheme since 1981 with nearly half of the county's parish churches now registered. The best sites for bees are those which are cut in rotation or infrequently, often having large ants' nests and moles which provide dry ground for nesting and warm microclimates. Lesser celandines and other spring flowers can be present even in regularly cut churchyards and daffodil patches protect these and other flowering plants from the mower for

Weybourne cliffs with daisy and thrift. The bare trampled ground is occupied by nesting aggregations of *Andrena humilis, A. thoracica, Dasypoda hirtipes, Colletes succinctus* and *Lasioglossum malachurum*

Weybourne beach with yellow horned-poppy and a south-facing bank used by many bee species for nesting

stems and are therefore largely absent from the coastal zone. *Colletes halophilus* has very large nesting colonies on dunes and the edges of saltmarsh creeks and uses sea aster as a pollen source. As in all *Colletes* species, *C. halophilus* lines its nest chambers with a waterproof secretion and its nests can survive inundation. The density of several bumblebee species is highest on the coastal fringe. *C. marginatus* and *C. fodiens* are coastal and Breckland species.

THE BROADS
This region is one of the British strongholds for *Macropis europaea*, which uses yellow loosestrife as a source of pollen and oils and for *Hylaeus pectoralis* which often uses empty *Lipara* galls in common reeds as a nest site. Unimproved grasslands such as those at Sutton Fen are important for species such as *Melitta leporina* and its cleptoparasite *Nomada flavopicta*. The banks of rivers and channels offer many Fabaceae, Apiaceae and Asteraceae food sources as well as bare ground for nest sites. These banks are used by many *Bombus* and *Andrena* species including *A. humilis*.

THE FENS
In the spring, willows and blackthorn offer abundant food sources for bees, with up to nine species of *Andrena* flying together in some

dunes dry out quickly when rainfall is low. Yellow Asteraceae bordering the north Norfolk Coastal Path attract bumblebees, *Lasioglossum* species and *Dasypoda hirtipes* in summer. *Megachile leachella* is largely a coastal species in Norfolk, though there are some records from the Brecks. *M. maritima* is frequent on the coast but also present inland at sandy sites, while *M. circumcincta* specialises on bird's-foot-trefoil in favoured spots. These leafcutter species nest in the ground, unlike several other leafcutters which require hollow

St Benet's Abbey grassland with meadow buttercup

Neep's Bridge and Middle Drain
with willows and grassy banks

locations. Drain margins and river banks provide plentiful nest sites. Later in the season fallow land and field margins provide nectar and pollen from arable weeds such as spear thistle, wild radish and scentless mayweed. *Andrena cineraria* and *A. flavipes* have colonised the area in the past 15 years. There are also good populations of the willow specialist *A. praecox* and its parasite *Nomada ferruginata*. *Osmia bicolor* is spreading into the area from the Brecks. The Fens are a stronghold for *Bombus ruderatus* with queens using the very large-growing white dead-nettle and other members of the Lamiaceae.

FARMLAND
More than half the land surface of Norfolk is arable fields. Much of farmland management in the county is aimed at game preservation, with wildlife conservation a secondary aim. This has resulted in the creation and preservation of much important bee habitat. Sugar beet, wheat and barley provide no flowers for bees, and crop sprays may be harmful. Insecticides and herbicides can drift on to field margins and hedgerows, making many arable fields a very poor bee habitat. Weeds can potentially provide pollen and nectar. A recent survey by the Norfolk Flora Group found that sugar beet is the crop with the highest number of arable plant (weed) species with the least being in cereals, and that light chalky soils have more species than other soil types. Disturbed areas at field entrances were also richer. Oilseed rape does offer a large amount of pollen and nectar from April to May and is used by several *Andrena* species, Honeybees and bumblebees, especially where woodlands and hedgerows are close-by. The crop does not require pollinators to set seed, but yields can be higher when insect pollinators are present. Orchards and soft fruit farms are dependent on suitable pollinators. *Osmia bicornis* and bumblebees can be better pollinators than Honeybees, having longer tongues and (in bumblebees) greater tolerance to cool conditions. They will only be present on fruit farms if other food sources are available outside the fruit flowering season. Arable 'weeds' are generally very scarce in Norfolk. Plants including poppies, thistles, sowthistles, mayweeds, corn marigold and wild radish can flourish in uncropped corners and field entrances. Uncropped field margins can provide perennial food sources such as bird's-foot-trefoil and clovers, but do not always remain long enough to become nutrient-poor and flower-rich. Bees take a while to colonise new sites and establish themselves; they cannot survive too much chopping and changing. Wildflower seed mixtures aimed at bees can be useful, but will not help if the area is ploughed and re-seeded too frequently, thereby destroying nest and hibernation sites.

Field margin with poppy, scentless mayweed,
thistles and scabious, Flitcham [RT]

Seeded wildflower Fenland corner with
phacelia and wild radish

Changes in bee habitats in Norfolk: historical perspectives

The distribution maps in the species accounts show where each bee species has been recorded across three time periods. They show that some species have become extinct, or declined considerably, since the first Norfolk recorders were active in the 19th century (see also Appendix 2). For bees which are still relatively common we are unable tell whether they have declined or not. It is difficult to picture the county as it might have been 100 years or more ago. Bee recorder Colbran Wainright describes West Runton from a visit in the summer of 1900. "These hills are richly clothed with woods, with pleasant open spaces, and everywhere was a great wealth of flowers of all kinds."

We can presume that bees recolonised these lands following the last Ice Age and that conditions have changed continually since that time. The first farmers are thought to have arrived 4,000–5,000 years ago. The following account is based largely on Gerry Barnes and Tom Williamson's *Rethinking Ancient Woodland*. Post-glacial mixed woodland was gradually eroded by farming activities which, by the Iron Age, resulted in widespread open agricultural landscapes in the county, even on heavy soils. But large areas of open heath and woodland persisted into the middle ages, especially along the clay soils of the central watershed, much of it probably used as wood pasture for domestic animals, including pigs. This was gradually enclosed as coppice woodland and deer parks from the 11th century onwards and wood pastures slowly declined. Open fields and commons were enclosed in piecemeal fashion in the south and east of the county, leading to complex patterns of ownership and generally small estates. On the lighter soils of the north and west, sheep were folded on the open heaths in order to improve soil fertility. Large estates evolved which had the resources to improve the poor soils, but with many areas remaining as open sheep walks until the 18th or 19th centuries. Faden's map of 1797 shows that 40% of Breckland was still open heath at this time. Major areas of heathland also persisted on the western greensands around King's Lynn, much of the land between Norwich and Holt and along the Cromer Ridge. About 30,000 hectares of heathland (8.4% of Norfolk's land area) remained in the county at the end of the 18th century and a similar area survived as unenclosed 'waste' and commons. Much of the heathland and common land is thought to have been partially wooded. The total of heather heathland in 2016 calculated by the Norfolk Biodiversity Information Service (NBIS) is just 1,137 hectares.

Norfolk's coppiced woodlands were first created from enclosure of wood pastures or deer parks in the 11th–13th centuries, though a proportion of Norfolk's surviving 'ancient' woods are now believed to be only 200–300 years old rather than pre-1600. The 16th and 17th centuries saw the drainage of the Fens followed by the loss of most of the river valley mires and bogs. In the 18th and 19th centuries a network of canals and railways appeared across the county which paradoxically now offer corridors of surviving semi-natural habitat. The advent of mechanical means of drainage in the 19th and 20th centuries led to the clearance of nearly all the wet and inaccessible corners of fields and the channelling of most of the rivers and drainage dykes. Selective herbicides removed flowering plants from nearly all pastures and most surviving hay meadows in the post-war years. Lawnmowers and strimmers now patrol gardens, golf courses and municipal land, giving plants little opportunity to flower.

Early farming activities were probably benign or even beneficial to wildlife, but in the past two centuries mechanisation and intensification have placed much of it under threat. Without any intention we created a bee paradise of meadows, heaths, woods and pastures but it now requires active intervention to avert the loss of many species. The following table summarises the percentage of land of different habitat types in Norfolk, based on remote sensing (NBIS). The figures reflect the extent to which Norfolk's varied habitats have been squeezed out by arable farmland, much of it now very species poor.

Habitat	% of land
Arable	62.7
Coastal and floodplain grazing marsh	3.3
Coastal saltmarsh	0.8
Coastal sand dunes	0.1
Coniferous plantation	1.8
Deciduous woodland	5.7
Fen, marsh and swamp	0.4
Humid dune slacks	0.0002
Lowland heathland with heather	0.2
Semi-improved grassland	5.1
Waterbodies	1.7
Urban, scrub, bare ground, improved grassland	18.2

Conserving Norfolk's bees

Why conserve bees? A bee visiting a flower is a wonderful sight, offering inspiration to artist and scientist alike. The importance of bees to the human food supply through pollination services has been well publicised and a large monetary value has been placed on the work they provide. But the economic argument should be a secondary one. We would not want to dispense with bees even if all crops were self-pollinated, as many are. Bees are unlikely all to disappear before humans, but we are losing the numbers and variety of bees. Their distribution is becoming more localised, risking the loss of wild flowers that depend on them for setting seed, thus impoverishing our lives.

Causes of decline Many of the causes of the decline and extinction of bees in Norfolk and elsewhere will be all too familiar to naturalists. The following is an attempt to summarise them:

- Loss of flower rich meadows, heathland and pastures through herbicide use and ploughing
- Cultivation of marginal land by drainage and general tidying up, facilitated by better machinery
- Use of inorganic fertilisers which have taken away the need for fallow fields/Brecks with the loss of mixed farms with livestock and high crop diversity
- Loss of woodland, orchards and hedgerows
- General nutrient enrichment by polluting nitrogen compounds causing rank vegetation to grow where once there were diverse flower rich verges and swards
- Loss of bare ground for nesting bees owing to a lack of poaching by livestock, upgrading of lanes to roads, more rank vegetation, fewer informal footpaths
- Over use of mowers and strimmers
- The decline of rabbits and an increase in deer
- Planting of showy flowers inappropriate for insects
- Use of insecticides
- Construction and urbanisation
- Climate change.

Government ambitions The conservation of bees is now high on the national agenda, thanks to warnings from scientists who have mapped and surveyed bee populations over many years, especially members of the Bees, Wasps and Ants Recording Society. The Government, through Defra, is committed to 'halt the overall loss of England's biodiversity by 2020'. In order to achieve this, a Natural Environment White Paper calls for 'a more integrated landscape-scale approach' to conservation. In 2015 Defra pledged £900 million for a new version of the Countryside Stewardship scheme for which 'bees and pollinators' are one of four priorities. The rationale is that habitat networks and corridors will allow wildlife to disperse in response to climate change and also provide various ecosystem services such as pollination, carbon storage and flood reduction. This has triggered several initiatives in Norfolk to provide more joined up wildlife habitat.

Reconnecting Norfolk's habitats Natural England (NE) is the body responsible for awarding Countryside Stewardship grants to landowners, based on a points system. Extra points are awarded for 'hotspots for wild pollinators and farmland birds'. For pollinators this is 'defined by 10 species of declining wild bee species associated with England's farmed landscapes'. Grants are awarded for sowing 'nectar flower mix', 'flower-rich margins and plots', 'two-year sown legume fallow', 'autumn sown bumblebird mix', 'legume and herb-rich swards', amongst others. These must be introduced on a minimum of 3% of the land area. NE apportions grants across 159 National Character Areas, seven being partly or entirely in Norfolk. As these do not conform to administrative areas, each of Norfolk's seven local councils has also drawn up their own ecological network maps for planning purposes. The Norfolk Biodiversity Partnership in the County Council is very active in coordinating and promoting conservation across Norfolk.

In the non-government sector, Norfolk Wildlife Trust (NWT) has developed its own Living Landscape plans. In NWT's words: "Living Landscapes aim to return biodiversity to our

Kelling Heath: Norfolk County Council has been involved in the restoration of this heath over the past 20 years

countryside by restoring, reconnecting and recreating wild areas. New nature-rich habitats will be created, joining together surviving refuges to allow wildlife species to move more freely and expand their range and populations. Often these Living Landscape areas will be close to where people live, allowing them to also benefit from and enjoy these natural spaces which, we hope, will soon become filled with wildlife". Eight areas are included with some excellent progress already made.

The charity Buglife is also involved in identifying habitat corridors in Norfolk, the intention being to connect the best insect habitats across each county. Norfolk's B-lines were mapped in 2016 by a group of specialists including the Norfolk Farming and Wildlife Advisory Group. Landowners within these zones are being encouraged to develop and connect wildflower-rich sites.

B-lines corridors in Norfolk

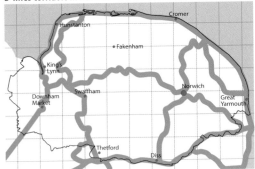

In 2014 the Heritage Lottery Fund granted £1.5 million to a landscape-scale project in Breckland called Breaking New Ground Landscape Partnership involving the Royal Society for the Protection of Birds, NWT and the Forestry Commission. One of its aims is to create more bare ground typical of past Breckland habitats, a need identified by the Breckland Biodiversity Audit carried out by the University of East Anglia. Part of this project involves disturbing the ground on ten percent of the area of the Ministry of Defence's Stanford Training Area, over a 10-year period. Bees should benefit from this by the provision of more nest sites and the growth of good pollen and nectar plants from dormant seed.

How are populations responding? The importance of habitat connectivity can be illustrated by looking at how one specialist bee species might behave. *Andrena fuscipes* uses only heather (ling) pollen. Heather now occurs in many isolated fragments across Norfolk covering an area estimated at only 1,137 hectares, compared with

343,210 hectares of arable land. If an *A. fuscipes* bee flies more than a kilometre or two from its birthplace, it is unlikely to find any heather and will not be able to feed or breed. This means that the remaining population will, on average, contain individuals which are less inclined to disperse; the individuals with the genes for dispersal (perhaps with longer wings and more get-up-and-go behaviour) will leave the population and not return, leaving the shorter-winged, less active individuals behind. For dispersal behaviour to be maintained, some of the dispersing insects (or their descendants) must return to the original population. This happens, for example, when Painted Lady butterflies make their way back to North Africa in the autumn. If this doesn't happen we end up with a population which will not, or cannot, fly very far and may become inbred. A healthy insect population is likely to consist of groups which disperse backwards and forwards between sites with suitable habitat. At any one time only a proportion of sites may be occupied, partly due to chance and partly because some sites become temporarily unsuitable. This dynamic state allows gene flow between populations, reducing inbreeding. A further advantage is that insects can get away from some of their parasites, by leaving them behind when they disperse. For example, it may take a while for *Nomada rufipes* to find a new colony of its *Andrena fuscipes* host. These ideas are speculative but it is generally accepted that to be sure of conserving species such as *A. fuscipes* we need to provide them with large areas of habitat and habitat stepping stones close enough to allow the populations to disperse between them.

Planting wildflower margins is likely to help widespread generalist bee species but will not greatly assist specialist bees such as *Andrena fuscipes*. A recent article co-authored by a sixty-strong international affiliation argues that strategies to promote crop pollination should target a different set of species than management to promote threatened bees. They suggest that pollination services arguments are not relevant to rare and specialised bee species.

The majority of extinct or scarce bees in Norfolk are heathland or grassland species. Bee species which use tree and shrub pollen are generally in a better position. To sustain Norfolk's specialist bees it will be necessary to revert arable land to heathland and to wildflower rich grassland on quite a large scale, reversing some of the losses over the past 200–300 years. Natural England is currently restoring and recreating some excellent chalk grassland in the county but their scope is limited by funding. The recent *State of Nature* report finds that 59% of British invertebrate species have declined since 1970. While public sympathy and general intentions are turning towards nature conservation, the ambition to halt further decline by 2020 will be difficult to meet. Some Government funding might more profitably go towards land acquisition for new national nature reserves rather than short term stewardship schemes. These reserves can be multi-purpose with space for recreation as well as conservation, ideally close to towns and villages as envisaged by the NWT's Living Landscape project.

Direct state funding for conservation is unlikely to be forthcoming in any quantity unless justified by clear economic imperatives. To conserve bees and other wildlife it will be necessary for conservationists increasingly to join forces with other bodies having shared or overlapping objectives. The Campaign to Protect Rural England seeks smaller, more diverse and sustainable farms, transparency about land ownership and a much higher proportion of public funding going directly to delivering public benefits. From 2008 the requirement to set aside a percentage of land for wildlife was dropped as food surpluses declined, but the taxpayer funded Basic Payment Scheme can be still be claimed for all land where agricultural activity is taking place. Land which has reverted to scrub is excluded meaning that farmers are cautious about leaving land uncultivated for any length of time. Incentives continue to encourage the tidying up of the landscape, increasing the area of cultivation and placing 'nature' in designated, rather small, parcels of land.

Our changing position in Europe offers an opportunity to redirect funding away from policies which have seen the loss of so much wildlife over the past 70 years. Conservationists who have lived through the second half of the 20th century have perhaps become too resigned to an attrition of the natural world, which is seen as an inevitable consequence of our growing population and high consumption. Yet many farsighted Norfolk landowners have demonstrated that productive farming and rich wildlife can co-exist. 88% of the bee species ever recorded in Norfolk have been seen post-2000. Knowing where these bees are and what their needs are is the key to conserving them better and encouraging the return of those which have been lost from the county.

Insecticides: a hidden menace Neonicotinoids have been much in the news. In Norfolk these insecticides are used as a seed dressing on a range of crops including winter barley to prevent damage from insect pests. There was particular concern about neonicotinoid use on oilseed rape to prevent soil aphid and flea beetle damage to autumn sown crops, because of the possibility of bees being contaminated by the insecticide when visiting rape flowers in the following year. Neonicotinoid use is currently banned on all flowering crops, though some local derogations for autumn sown oilseed rape have been in place in the past two years. The insecticide can persist in the soil and may spread beyond the field boundary. Dave Goulson describes experimental evidence that neonicotinoids can have an adverse effect on bee behaviour in sub-lethal doses, which can damage their abililty to learn and to navigate (see Bees and flowers p.30). If neonicotinoids are not used then other insecticides may be substituted which could be worse. These problems illustrate the difficulties of conservation in an agricultural landscape such as Norfolk. It is a balancing act which may be perfected only through better science and more subtle ways of reducing insect damage.

Herbicides Selective herbicides may be having an even greater impact on bee populations than insecticides because they destroy flowering plants in pastures, crops and gardens on a vast scale, depriving bees of their food source. It is now very difficult to imagine how the countryside looked before these herbicides were developed. New generations are unaware of what they have lost.

The importance of stability Environmental incentives need to be long term. Some stewardship margins which were steadily becoming nutrient poor but rich in clovers and trefoils are now being ploughed to plant wildflower seed mixes. Bee nests will have been destroyed for little or no gain. Old grasslands develop uneven surfaces through the actions of moles and ants. In the author's garden it has taken ten years to grow a *Lasius flavus* ant hill of 60 cm diameter and 30 cm height. Uneven topography provides microclimates varying in aspect and water supply and supporting a much wider diversity of plants than a flat surface. Such grasslands are now rare but can be found in some churchyards, grazed unimproved grasslands and old orchards. Bees tend to return to the nest sites from where they emerged and some nest aggregations last for decades. New habitat is best provided alongside established features such as Peddars Way, earthworks, ancient woodland, heathland, old chalk grassland and scrub (an under-appreciated habitat). This gives the best chance of colonisation from established populations and also buffers the most diverse existing habitats. Often the ideal management is simply to leave the land to go through succession without planting anything. This way the plants will be from local seed and establish at varying times making a rich mosaic.

We are a crowded country and each of us has different ideals for the same bits of land.

Some prefer to plant the roadsides with daffodils, palm trees and ornamental grasses. Others prefer dandelions, gorse bushes and scabious. It may look scruffy, but look closely and you will see bees collecting pollen and excavating nest holes in the patchy grass, as they have done for millions of years. Once gone they will never come back.

Can we change some of this – an arable field in north Norfolk [DO]

... into this? Recreated chalk grassland in Hampshire developed from arable fields by the charity Butterfly Conservation

Nests and life cycle

Bees are herbivores, using nectar for energy and pollen as a source of protein for the developing larvae. By contrast nearly all wasps are carnivores, placing their eggs on the bodies of insects and other prey, which they paralyse with a sting. Bees use their stings only for defence.

The nests of bees attract a wide variety of parasites which attempt to take over their food store or attack their larvae. The nesting behaviour of food collecting bees is adapted to avoiding such attacks in various ways:

- Pollen is placed out of sight in places such as chambers under the ground or hollows in walls or stems.
- Bees arriving with pollen often zig-zag around before plunging quickly into their nest holes, thereby reducing the chances of being followed by a cleptoparasite.
- Some mining bees cover their nest holes before leaving. Others burrow into loose sand which collapses when they leave, obscuring the entrance. Leafcutter bees finish their completed nest with a cavity and a further covering of leaf material which reduces the chances of a *Coelioxys* bee inserting an egg.
- Bees sometimes physically attack cleptoparasites. Cleptoparasites are protected by a thick cuticle, presumably selected as a means of resisting such attacks.

Attracting a mate Chemical signals which travel in the air (pheromones) are of great importance to bees and although not usually detectable by humans, there are some clues that field observers can see. Male bees pause in their flights on leaves and stems, depositing scents which attract females or other males. Darwin watched male bumblebees doing this and recruited five of his children to note when a bee paused and buzzed at a particular point along his sand walk. Although he did not observe queen bumblebees visiting these spots, it is now thought that virgin queens are attracted to them for mating. Some *Andrena* males behave in a similar way. *Lasioglossum* males sometimes cluster together on plant stems, perhaps combining their pheromone emissions.

Mating Mating strategies vary between species. *Megachile maritima* and *Anthidium manicatum* males hold territories and monopolise females which enter them. These bees will fly at any large insect passing by, sometimes gripping it and dropping to the ground. *Mechachile maritima* tackle bumblebees in this way. This could be mating attempts which sometimes pick the wrong target. It is also possible that the behaviour reduces the depletion of pollen and nectar in an area, making females more likely to spend time there.

Unmated female bees release pheromone attractants which are species specific. Once coupled to a female, male bees stay in place for several minutes. Males of some species continue to make mating attempts with mated females even though they are collecting pollen. *Macropis europaea* males pounce on females as they visit yellow loosestrife flowers. They have thick muscular legs which may be an adaptation for clinging to females. *Panurgus banksianus* males behave similarly. These attempts seem to be resisted.

Part of a cluster of *Lasioglossum calceatum* ♂s, Thriplow, Cambridgeshire, 9 August [RGC]

Mating attempt by ♂ *Macropis europaea*, Cambridge Botanic Garden, 23 July

Mating cluster of *Panurgus banksianus*, Kelling Heath, 18 July

Andrena humilis mating, Weybourne, May

Male or female? Female bees generally mate once and the sperm is stored inside the abdomen. This store can last many weeks or months. In bumblebees, *Halictus* and *Lasioglossum*, mated females survive the winter and all males die off. The sperm store lasts until the spring when the females start nesting. In all bees, wasps and ants, fertilised eggs develop into females and unfertilised eggs into males.

Mining bees Many members of the genera *Andrena, Anthophora, Colletes, Dasypoda, Halictus, Lasioglossum* and *Melitta* excavate a nest in the ground using their mandibles. The nest hole can be up to 30 cm in length and can be horizontal or vertical. Side chambers are excavated and lined with glandular secretions which deter fungi and act as waterproofing. A ball of pollen mixed with nectar is stored inside, then an egg is laid on the food store and the chamber is sealed with earth. New adult bees may leave the nest later in the same year. Alternatively they may hibernate while immature and emerge in the following year. Adults live for up to about four weeks, and females spend much of this time underground in the nest.

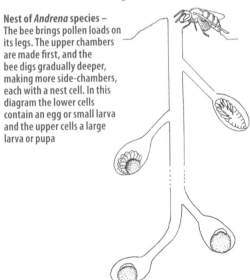

Nest of *Andrena* species – The bee brings pollen loads on its legs. The upper chambers are made first, and the bee digs gradually deeper, making more side-chambers, each with a nest cell. In this diagram the lower cells contain an egg or small larva and the upper cells a large larva or pupa

Males of many species have white marks on their faces. Amongst *Andrena* bees this seems to be associated with species where the males face off each other when they meet, and it may be a signal of aggression.

Male bees generally hatch a week or so before females. A strategy used by some males is to wait at nest aggregations for females to emerge or even enter nest holes to find them. This happens in *Anthophora plumipes, Colletes succinctus* and *Osmia* species amongst others. *Bombus hypnorum* males try to enter other nests to find emerging queens but are often repelled by the home workers, leading to a swarm of circling insects around the nest entrance.

Mason bees Members of the family Megachilidae gather various materials to make nest partitions and nest linings rather than using their own secretions. The genera involved (materials used in brackets) are: *Anthidium* (plant hairs), *Chelostoma* (soil and honey), *Heriades* (resin), *Hoplitis* (leaf mastic), *Megachile* (cut leaves) and *Osmia* (mud or leaf mastic). The nest is made inside a stem, a hole in the ground, a snail shell or other hollow space. New adults usually emerge in the following year.

Anthophora plumipes nesting aggregation at Weybourne, 6 May

Megachile sp. ♀ with piece of cut leaf, Weybourne, 30 July

Old nest chambers

Megachile ligniseca ♀ cutting a leaf, Thriplow, Cambridgeshire, 13 August

J H Fabre carried out ingenious experiments with *Osmia* bees in the early 20th century. He found that around 15 eggs were laid by each bee, not necessarily all in the same cavity. Larger cells were made first and received more food stocks and smaller cells were made towards the outside with less food, regardless of how many cells were in the cavity. Females developed from the larger inner cells and males from the smaller outer cells. He demonstrated that female bees could determine the sex of each egg as it was laid and explained the necessity for outer cells producing males, which emerge a week or more before females.

Pieces cut from rose leaves by a leafcutter bee. Oval pieces line the nest hole and round pieces cover the ends of each cell

Nest of *Osmia bicornis* – the bee is scraping pollen from the pollen hairs beneath the abdomen with her hind legs. Two cells are shown each with its food store and an egg. The partitions are made of mud

Social behaviour Some members of the genera *Halictus* and *Lasioglossum* show social behaviour with a large female laying eggs and smaller sterile females working for her in the nest and collecting food. Common examples in Norfolk are *Halictus rubicundus* and *Lasioglossum calceatum*. These bees have been the subject of research into the evolution of bee social behaviour. In the north of Britain *L. calceatum* nests solitarily, suggesting that the behaviour is adapted to local conditions. Bumblebees and Honeybees are more familiar examples of bee social behaviour: their life cycles are described in the species accounts.

Cleptoparasites, parasitoids and predators of bees

Cleptoparasites are cuckoos which live off the food collected by other species. Parasitoids eat the tissues of a larva or pupa of another species and eventually kill it. Predators hunt, kill and eat their prey. Sometimes the distinction between these three groups can be unclear. The most relevant here are the cleptoparasitic bees which invade the nests of other bees. While watching bees it is also likely that various parasitoids and predators will be seen, and some of the commoner Norfolk species are described below. The behaviour of nesting bees is well worth watching. Many of their actions are geared towards avoiding the attentions of species which might do them harm. It is easy to think of parasites as unpleasant hangers-on, too lazy to do their own work, but they are every bit as interesting and worthy of conservation as their hosts and, of course, they do not share our moral perspectives. The majority of species in the world are parasites of some kind. They can thrive only when their host populations are strong.

CLEPTOPARASITES

Fifty-six of Norfolk's 197 bee species (28%) are cleptoparasites, also called cuckoo bees. They collect no pollen themselves, instead laying their eggs in the nests of foraging bees, called their host. The larva of the cleptoparasite destroys the egg or larva of the host then develops into an adult by consuming the pollen and nectar store itself. Several cleptoparasitic bees have become very scarce or extinct in the county, perhaps indicating a declining host population. However, they can easily be missed because they are secretive and spend a lot of time waiting and watching nests rather than flying about collecting food. Cleptoparasitic bee genera in Norfolk are *Bombus* (six species out of 18) and all species of *Coelioxys*, *Epeolus*, *Melecta*, *Nomada*, *Sphecodes* and *Stelis*. Most are specific to one or two host species. All have probably evolved from pollen collecting species, but they are not necessarily closely related to their hosts.

Cleptoparasitic bees have very little hair, since they do not require it for pollen collecting: cuckoo bumblebees have thinner hair than other bumblebees. Pollen on the body is probably a disadvantage in flight if not combed off, and there has probably been selection to lose hair. Parasitic bees all have a relatively thick cuticle and strong mandibles which act as protection against possible attack from host bees.

British cuckoo bumblebees have hair colours which resemble their particular host, often quite closely, though they probably did not evolve directly from them. This mimicry may have nothing to do with being unobserved in the nest, which is usually dark, but instead be a form of Müllerian mimicry by which the cuckoo and its host share a warning colour pattern. This type of mimicry involves 'mimicry rings' which is a group of harmful species (in this case having a sting) sharing a warning colouration such as red and yellow or red and black. It is thought that predators will more quickly learn that bees sharing a particular colour pattern are dangerous and avoid eating them. It must be added that male bees have no sting, so gain an advantage by looking like females: a form of Batesian mimicry! Many *Nomada* species are mimics of the warning colouration of wasps, having black and yellow stripes with varying amounts of red. Nearly all *Sphecodes* species are black and red, which is probably also a warning colouration to potential predators. Members of the genera *Coelioxys*, *Epeolus*, *Melecta* and *Stelis* mostly have a body pattern which includes constrasting white bars or spots on a dark background for reasons which are not clear.

Cleptoparasites are often seen at the nest sites of possible hosts. However, there is still a lot of uncertainty about the host species of many cleptoparasitic bees, partly because bees often nest in mixed species aggregations. Ideally a bee nest should be collected and kept in an enclosed space until possible parasites hatch out. This is much more easily done with stem nesting bees than ground nesting ones. Clues of the host of a particular cleptoparasite can come from less direct evidence, for example:

- The parasite and host appear at the same time of year
- Host and parasite show matching changes in population, increasing or decreasing together
- The distribution of parasite and host is similar.

Quite often there is a mismatch between the distribution of a known cleptoparasite and its host. For example *Nomada signata* is confined to the Brecks in Norfolk but its host, *Andrena fulva*, is widespread. Hosts can develop an ability to deter their parasites and become free of them or almost so. In time their defences lapse or the parasite gets round them and the parasite returns, so we might see an ebb and flow of the host/parasite pair. Although *N. signata* is currently rare, *A. fulva* continues to be attacked by *N. panzeri*, which remains common. There may be

Comparisons of the distribution of possible cleptoparasite and host pairs in Norfolk (cleptoparasites on the left)

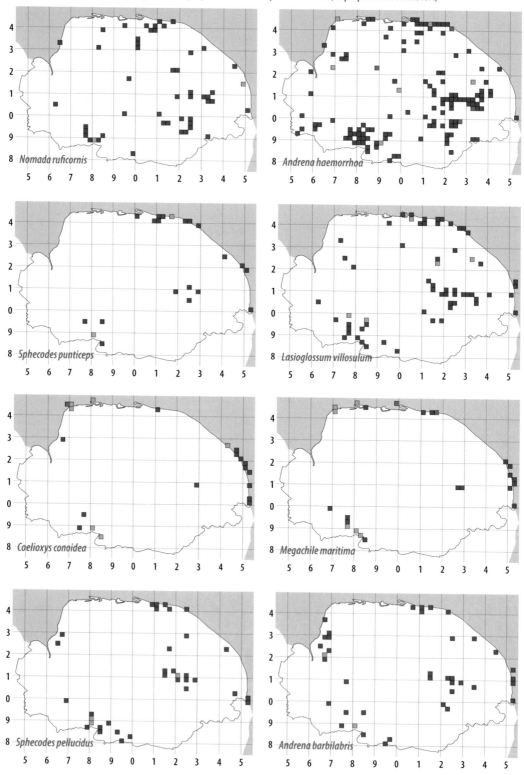

competition between the two nomad bees which complicates things further! Another example is *Bombus lapidarius* and its cuckoo bumblebee *B. rupestris*. The latter became very scarce in Norfolk and elsewhere from the 1940s up to the turn of the century (Plowright observed only two in his detailed studies in the 1960s), but it has now become widespread again. This could be through an 'arms race' between parasite and host but the exact causes of such changes are very hard to determine. Human impacts on bee populations are superimposed on 'natural' causes of population change such as these, and this makes assessing the effects of human pressures on the environment very difficult.

Cacoxenus indagator This is a small fly in the family Drosophilidae, known as fruit flies. It does not lay its eggs in fruit, however, but in the food stores in the nests of *Osmia* species, especially *O. bicornis*. It places its eggs in partially completed nests while the host is absent. Several eggs are laid in one nest cell and hatch into larvae which eat the food store. The host larva may be partially starved and reduced in size or even starved to death. The *Cacoxenus* flies emerge the following spring but may find themselves walled in by the nest partitions. The inflatable sac or ptilinum on its head, which flies use to emerge from the pupa, has extra strength and can break holes in the nest partitions. The fly shares the ability of its host to find the correct direction to break out based on the curvature of the cell partitions, which is convex on the exit side. New bee hotels usually develop strong populations of *O. bicornis* in the first year or two, but thereafter their numbers tend to stabilise or decline owing to the attentions of various invaders such as these.

Leucophora sp. ♀ waiting as a ♀ *Andrena clarkella* emerges from its nest hole, Kelling Heath, 20 April

Leucophora spp. and Miltogramma spp. These shadow flies are cleptoparasites and behave in a similar way to *Cacoxenus*, but are usually seen at the nests of mining bees such as *Andrena* and *Colletes*. The flies wait by nesting aggregations, watching for arriving bees laden with pollen. As a laden bee arrives, the shadow fly tails its movements. When the bee enters its nest the fly waits motionless near the nest entrance, and when the bee leaves the fly enters to lay its eggs on the pollen store.

Sapyga quinquepunctata This wasp is a cleptoparasite of mason bees such as *Osmia bicornis*, *O. leaiana* and *O. caerulescens*. It lays an egg in a nest cell of its host. The first stage of the wasp larva has large jaws which it uses to destroy the host egg. Later stages have smaller jaws and feed on the pollen store.

Cacoxenus indagator at *Osmia bicornis* nest in bee hotel, Weybourne, 14 May

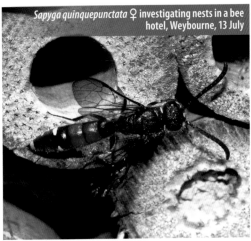
Sapyga quinquepunctata ♀ investigating nests in a bee hotel, Weybourne, 13 July

PARASITOIDS

Bee flies The bee fly *Bombylius major* is a common insect in Norfolk, often seen in gardens probing spring flowers with its long straight tongue, rather like a minute hummingbird. The flies lay their eggs in or near the nests of solitary bees of several species, especially *Andrena* bees. The larva of the fly then feeds on the bee larva, ultimately killing it.

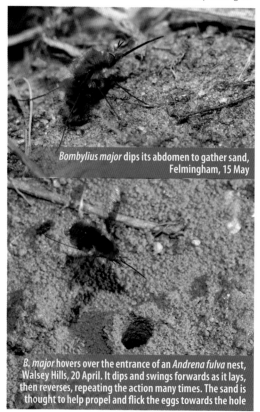

Bombylius major dips its abdomen to gather sand, Felmingham, 15 May

B. major hovers over the entrance of an *Andrena fulva* nest, Walsey Hills, 20 April. It dips and swings forwards as it lays, then reverses, repeating the action many times. The sand is thought to help propel and flick the eggs towards the hole

Stylopised *Andrena scotica* ♀ with reduced tibial hairs and small size, 14 March

Stylops

Sicus ferrugineus Weybourne, 23 July

Stylops Females of these parasitoids can be seen sandwiched between the abdomen segments of solitary bees. As the host bee visits a flower, small larvae with legs are released by the female and these crawl on to other bees visiting same flower. The larvae are carried back to the bee's nest where they find bee larvae, burrow inside them and feed on the tissues. On becoming adults, female *Stylops* adopt the sandwiched position again while males fly free, seeking females on other bees to mate with. Parasitised bees are said to be 'stylopised'. Stylopised female bees lose their pollen hairs and resemble males, while males tend to become larger and look more like females. These changes may facilitate the dispersal of *Stylops* larvae since the bees will spend most of their time taking nectar from flowers and not spend time in nest holes or seeking mates. Some bee species are

stylopised more often than others and there are several *Stylops* species, probably with specific hosts. This parasitism inevitably reduces the fecundity of a population.

Conopid flies – *Sicus ferrugineus* These flies wait on vegetation for bees, often a bumblebee. They leap on the bee and insert an egg between the tergites, using the curved abdomen. A larva develops inside the living bee gradually consuming it. When the bee dies the larva pupates.

PREDATORS

Cerceris rybyensis This is a wasp which actively hunts small bees. The bee is immediately stung and paralysed, then taken in to a nest hole in the ground where the wasp lays eggs in it. The eggs hatch into wasp larvae which feed on the

Cerceris rybyensis ♀ with captured *Halictus rubicundus* female, Kelling Heath, 26 July

Philanthus triangulum ♀ with Honeybee prey, Weybourne cliff, 12 August

paralysed bee. In Norfolk, bees from the genera *Lasioglossum*, *Halictus*, *Colletes* or *Andrena* have been recorded as prey. The wasp is quite common, so can have an impact on the bee population.

Bee Wolf *Philanthus triangulum* This wasp behaves in a similar way to the above species but takes only Honeybees. It can nest in large aggregations and these can make a considerable impact on Honeybee numbers.

Spiders Mining bees can be vulnerable to spiders when the bees visit their nest holes, especially if these are in banks with overhanging vegetation.

Bumblebees are often taken by crab spiders (family Thomisidae) which wait on flower heads and are often camouflaged

Andrena fuscipes ♀ taken by Snake-back Spider *Segestria senoculata*, Kelling Heath, August [RT]

Crab spider *Misumena vatia* with *Bombus terrestris* prey, East Ruston garden, 16 July

Bees and flowers in Norfolk

The colours and forms of flowers tell the story of thousands of years of co-evolution with pollinators, which are very often bees. Flowers entice insects to carry pollen to other flowers of the same species with the minimum reward to the pollen vector. Some flowers offer no reward at all and trick insects in to doing the work. Bees are adapted to gathering and transporting the most pollen and nectar of the highest quality with the minimum of energy expenditure. There is therefore a perpetual evolutionary conflict between flowers and bees. Flowers are, of course, complex and varied, making this an enormous subject. It is further complicated by the garden flower varieties available to bees. In the 1870s, Bridgman found the flowers most frequented by bees around Norwich to be "willows, sallows, blackthorn, dandelions, veronica, sycamore, brambles, thistles, ragwort, hawkweed, heath and the umbelliferae". Here, some examples are given of bee–flower interactions in the county, looking at how bees exploit flowers and to what extent particular flowers are dependent on visiting bees for pollination.

Heather (ling) *Calluna vulgaris* *Andrena fuscipes* (Heather Mining Bee) depends almost entirely on heather pollen. Bees fly and crawl around the heather flowers seeking nectar and as they do so become covered in the small white pollen grains of this plant. Pollen is combed off the body by the metatarsi and placed in the pollen carrying hairs of the hind legs. These comprise the tibia hairs, in the

form of a brush, the floccus hairs forming a basket on the femur and the propodeum pollen baskets under the central part of the bee, at the base of each hind leg.

Colletes succinctus (Heather Colletes) is on the wing at the same time as *A. fuscipes* and is also a heather specialist. Many bumblebee species use heather but the long-tongued species such as *Bombus hortorum* and *B. pascuorum* are less adept at accessing these small flowers. If not carried by insects, heather pollen can be dispersed by the wind, so heather might manage without the bees, but some bees are entirely dependent on heather.

Alexanders *Smyrnium olusatrum* This plant was reportedly introduced by the Romans. It is said to have been used by country people as a vegetable for many centuries until celery gradually replaced it. Its luxuriant spring growth along Norfolk's verges is usually a sign that the coast is near, but the species is now appearing inland too. It is a good nectar source for a variety of insects. The nectar appears rather glutinous and the plant's strategy may be that pollen sticks on a bee's face and is difficult to transfer to the pollen hairs. Pollen will be transferred from the face to stigmas of other flowers as the bee seeks more nectar. The dominance of alexanders in Norfolk may be a mixed blessing for bees since it supresses other spring flowers and probably offers a lot of nectar but rather little easily gathered pollen. Hogweed is a more prolific pollen source but flowers later.

Andrena fuscipes: much of the heather pollen gathers on the facial hairs. Pollen is passed backwards from leg to leg. This ♀ is transferring pollen from her face with a front leg while simultaneously passing pollen from a middle to a back leg. Tibia hairs and the floccus are becoming loaded with pollen

Andrena dorsata ♀ on alexanders, Walsey Hills, 18 April. A little pollen his been gathered on the legs but a lot is stuck to the face

Andrena clarkella ♀ with nectar added to willow pollen, making it darker. Beeston Common, 19 March

A. clarkella taking nectar from ♀ pussy willow, Kelling Heath, 7 April. Stigmas are touching pollen-laden hairs on the bee

A. clarkella on ♂ pussy willow, Kelling Heath, 7 April

Bombus lucorum queen taking nectar from ♂ pussy willow, Kelling Heath, 5 April. On emerging, queens seek only nectar: they start gathering pollen when a nest has been established

Willows *Salix* spp. The willow family is associated with wet places, especially the Fens, the Broads and riverbanks generally. Worked-out gravel and sand workings are often surrounded by willows and Willow Lines were widely planted and maintained as pollards along roads as bank retainers in the Broads in the 19th century. Willows are also a common feature of damp woodland. Willows are generally spring flowering but some species have an additional summer season. Male and female catkins (pussy willows) grow on separate trees. Female catkins offer nectar, thereby attracting bees to them which may have visited male catkins previously. Willow pollen is very small and in some, such as goat willow, the flowers appear before the leaves, all features indicating an evolutionary transition from wind to insect pollen transport. It is likely that willows are highly dependent on insects for pollen transfer, though some pollen can be transferred by the wind.

Four Norfolk bee species depend almost exclusively on willow pollen: *Andrena clarkella*, *A. praecox*, *A. tibialis* and *Colletes cunicularius*, this last species having recently arrived in Norfolk. A further eleven *Andrena* species have been observed on willows in the county and willows are also of great importance to spring queen bumblebees, with ten species observed on them. The three *Andrena* species have fairly simple tibia hairs (see illustration p.26) and rely partly on the small pollen grains packing together and sticking to each other. *A. clarkella* does sometimes add nectar to the pollen mass. All have well developed flocci and propodeal pollen baskets.

Asteraceae Asteraceae such as ragwort, cat's-ear, dandelion, hawk's-beards, hawkweeds and hawkbits provide a lot of pollen for bees and are some of the commonest and most widespread plants in the county. Their composite flower structure ensures that pollen and nectar are available in large quantities. However, not all bees use these flowers. *Osmia bicornis* (Red Mason Bee) does not use it even though it feeds on a very wide range of other flower species, though *O. leaiana* and *O. spinulosus* do. *Colletes daviesanus*, *C. fodiens*, *C. halophilus*, *C. similis* and *C. succinctus* all use Asteraceae pollen while *C. cunicularius*, *C. marginatus* and *C. hederae* generally do not. *Andrena denticulata* and *A. humilis* specialise in Asteraceae pollen but many *Andrena* species avoid it. Asteraceae pollen is large and spiky and may be difficult to digest. It is thought to contain toxins, perhaps alkaloids. Bees which use it are presumed to have specialisations allowing them to overcome these defences. When fed to larvae of bee species which do not use Asteraceae pollen the larvae do not develop. By this means Asteraceae restrict the bees visiting their flowers, improving the chances of pollen transport to other plants of the same species. This probably works well with yellow Asteraceae as different species tend to come into flower in succession through the year.

Asteraceae have declined greatly in Norfolk as grasslands have been lost or tidied up. Ragwort is the victim of some over-zealous control, even on protected land, on the basis of its toxicity when eaten by livestock, which generally happens only when provided in cut hay. The plant has acquired a bad name despite its great importance to insects. A recent Friends of the Earth document shows that the dangers of the plant can be exaggerated and the laws applying to it misinterpreted. *Andrena tridentata* was once commonly seen on ragwort in Norfolk but is now extinct in the British Isles. Thistles are similarly persecuted: bumblebees and *Megachile* bees rely on them.

Scabious *Andrena hattorfiana* (Large Scabious Mining Bee) and *A. marginata* (Small Scabious Mining Bee) both use the pollen of field scabious *Knautia arvensis* and small scabious *Scabiosa columbaria* and rarely any other. The scabious plants however are visited by a wide range of other insects and do not depend on these bees exclusively. The benefit for the bees is that they are adept at collecting this pollen rapidly by virtue of their specialised pollen hairs. They also have a long tongue capable of reaching nectar deep in the flower. The timing of emergence of these bees in July coincides with the flowering of scabious.

Panurgus banksianus ♀ gathering pollen from cat's-ear, Kelling Heath, 11.58 am, 28 July. These flowers close in the afternoon and the bees do all their pollen gathering in the mornings

Asteraceae pollen sticks together easily. Mating attempt by *Panurgus banksianus*

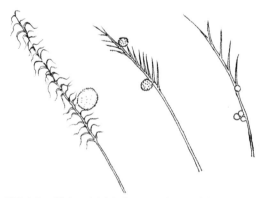

Tibia hairs of (left to right) *Andrena marginata* with field scabious pollen, *A. denticulata* with ragwort pollen and *A. praecox* with willow pollen. The smaller pollens may be attached electrostatically, while the scabious pollen is netted by the hairs. Bees are the only insects with branched hairs

Andrena marginata ♀ on field scabious, Weybourne, 3 August, with large pink pollen grains caught among the feathery tibia hairs

Foxglove *Digitalis purpurea* *A Flora of Norfolk* quotes William Turner, herbalist, 1548 as noting that foxgloves are "much in England and especially in Norfolk". The main visitors to foxgloves are bumblebees, including males, especially the long-tongued species *Bombus hortorum*, *B. pascuorum* and *B. ruderatus* seeking nectar. On emerging from a flower, a bumblebee usually moves up the spike to the next one, this being the easiest way to move between the downward pointing flowers. The upper flowers are in the male stage, releasing pollen, which is dusted on the bumblebee's thorax. Having reached the top, it generally flies down to a low flower on the next flower spike. The lower flowers are older and have receptive stigmas which receive pollen from the bee's thorax. In this way the structure of the plant facilitates cross pollination. The bumblebees usually move from plant to plant and this reduces any waste of pollen by the plant that would happen if the bees visited other species.

A. marginata ♂ on field scabious showing its long tongue, Weybourne Camp, 3 August

Foxgloves Kelling Heath, June. This plant is generally associated with neutral to acid soils

Andrena hattorfiana sorting out a field scabious pollen load before flying to its nest, Weybourne Camp, 27 July

Bombus hortorum in foxglove, Northamptonshire, 18 June

Bombus lucorum collecting pollen from western gorse, Kelling Heath, August [RGC]

Honeybee worker on gorse with gorse pollen moistened with nectar in its pollen baskets, Kelling Heath, 14 February

Gorse *Ulex europaeus* and western gorse *U. gallii* Gorse flowers can be seen almost throughout the year on some Norfolk heaths, a summer gap in common gorse being filled by western gorse. The common gorse is present throughout the county except on wet areas such as the Fens. The flowers produce large quantities of orange-yellow pollen, but little or no nectar, despite their strong coconut smell. They are visited by at least eight *Andrena* species, *Anthophora plumipes*, Honeybees, *Bombus lapidarius*, *B. lucorum*, *B. pascuorum*, *B. pratorum*, *B. terrestris*, *B. vestalis*, *Lasioglossum parvulum*, *L. punctatissimum* and *Nomada goodeniana*. The weight of larger bees can force open the paired keel petals allowing the anthers to spring upwards, placing

A newly emerged *Bombus pascuorum* queen seeking nectar on gorse (and probably not finding any), Holt Lowes, March 2012. The anthers and stigma have sprung upwards from the keel petals

Andrena ovatula with gorse pollen, Kelling Heath, 21 June

pollen on the bee. Bees are said to seek unsprung flowers. *Andrena bimaculata* (Large Gorse Mining Bee) and *A. ovatula* (Small Gorse Mining Bee) are so named because of their particular liking for gorse. Gorse flowers can self-fertilise but the transport of pollen between plants by bees will presumably reduce inbreeding.

Brambles *Rubus* spp. Bramble's peak flowering season in midsummer provides a reliable source of nectar and pollen in almost every wayside and hedgerow, attracting bees of all sizes and tongue length. The flowers are especially attractive to bumblebees including cuckoo bumblebees (for nectar). Several second brood *Andrena* species use bramble pollen including *A. bimaculata*, *A. dorsata*, *A. minutula* and *A. thoracica*. It is also used by some *Hylaeus* and *Lasioglossum* species. Norfolk's bramble expert Alec Bull tells us that most brambles are apomictic, producing seeds without the need for fertilisation of the egg cell in the ovule. This breeding system has resulted in the formation of many separate genetic forms with over 300 micro-species in the British Isles, 100 of them in Norfolk, more than in adjacent counties. These species generally produce clones. However, the commonest micro-species in Norfolk, *Rubus ulmifolius* can produce seeds in the conventional way and is very varied. It is also the best source of blackberries. Studies show that blackberries form just as well when insects are excluded from the flowers, but this needs testing with respect to the various micro-species concerned. The quantity of nectar produced by *R. ulmifolius* suggests that these brambles need insects.

Lasioglossum sp. collecting pollen from a fully opened *Rubus ulmifolius* flower. It is using the outer anthers which have dehisced. Weybourne Camp, 27 July

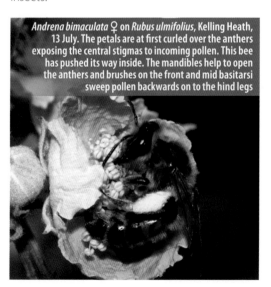

Andrena bimaculata ♀ on *Rubus ulmifolius*, Kelling Heath, 13 July. The petals are at first curled over the anthers exposing the central stigmas to incoming pollen. This bee has pushed its way inside. The mandibles help to open the anthers and brushes on the front and mid basitarsi sweep pollen backwards on to the hind legs

Bombus hypnorum queen seeking nectar, Beeston Common, 10 July

CAN BEES ADAPT TO NEW POLLEN SOURCES?

Melitta haemorrhoidalis and *Chelostoma campanularum* use only bellflower, Campanulaceae, pollen to stock their nests. Bridgman recorded them in Norfolk the 1870s on the same flowers that they use today. Newly emerged *Chelostoma* have an inherited preference for the colours and scents of bellflowers. As described above, bees also have structural adaptations suiting them to particular pollen sources. But some bees with narrow pollen preferences seem able to modify their food choices. In *Colletes* bees the food given as a larva can determine the food plant they seek as newly emerged adults and this genus seems to be actively evolving. Adult bees, especially those using a wide range of flowers, are able to modify their feeding choices through experience and may develop different flower preferences for nectar and pollen. Garden flowers are readily used if they are found to offer good food rewards. Bees learn to navigate to and from their nests or hives and bumblebees can hold a map in their heads of the locations of individual plants. The ability to learn and navigate can be damaged by neonicotinoid insectides, which target the insects' nervous system (see p.14).

A recent study of two long-tongued alpine bumblebee species in Colorado revealed a reduction in mean tongue length of nearly 25% over 40 years, thought to be in response to changes in the range of flowers available as the climate warms. This is a surprisingly rapid genetic response to environmental change. We can expect some bee species and populations to be more adaptable than others and this will determine how well they cope with human impacts on their environment. Amateur bee watchers are well placed to discover more about bee flower choices and how they develop.

GENETIC VARIATION IN NORFOLK'S BEES

Adapting to changes in climate and flower communities depends on bee populations having plenty of genetic diversity. This could be assessed by DNA studies but some clues come from visible variation in bees. *Andrena marginata* females have bright orange on parts of the abdomen but this grades into individuals which are almost entirely dark. The same range of colour forms occurs today as in Ken Durrant's collection from the 1980s suggesting that populations retain similar genetic diversity.

Bombus hortorum queen visiting early-purple orchid, Swanton Novers Great Wood, 13 May. This orchid offers no nectar; only recently emerged naïve bees visit the plant, then quickly learn to ignore it, but often not before they have tried a few flowers and transported their pollen

Andrena bimaculata plain (above) and red (below) forms. In Bridgman's time these were considered to be different species

Sometimes there are differences between first and second broods. *Andrena minutula* males have black hair on their faces in the first brood but pale hair in the second. *Andrena bimaculata* was divided into three species in Bridgman's time in the 19th century. Red forms were thought to be a different species and the second brood was given a different species name from the first. It is not always certain that second broods are the offspring of first broods: they may be a different population with an annual life cycle emerging later in the year and somewhat genetically distinct. There is also some influence of temperature on cuticle colours.

Colletes bees have diverged into a range of species with different food preferences, each emerging at a time which coincides with its main pollen source. *C. cunicularius* and *C. hederae* have recently arrived in the county, each exploiting a food source not used by other *Colletes*. They seem to be increasing quite rapidly, perhaps assisted by milder conditions in spring and autumn.

In general we can say that bees differ in their behavioural flexibility, with the more specialised bees being the most vulnerable to environmental change and degradation. Flowers can also potentially adapt in response to changes in bee visits. Some flowers can cash in on others which give greater rewards by matching their flowering times or mimicking their flower structure. *Rubus* species may have become apomictic when pollinators were scarce during the Ice Age.

Species	Main food plant	Emergence	Main habitat
Colletes cunicularius	Willows	April–May	River banks and sand pits
Colletes daviesanus	Yellow Asteraceae	June–September	Field margins, gardens.
Colletes fodiens	Ragwort, tansy, etc	July–September	Sandy soils
Colletes halophilus	Sea aster	August–October	Salt marshes and sand dunes
Colletes hederae	Ivy	September–November	Widespread
Colletes marginatus	Wild mignonette, etc	June–August	Coast and Brecks
Colletes similis	Yellow Asteraceae	June–September	Light soils including coast
Colletes succinctus	Heather	July–September	Heathland

Explanation of the species accounts

All bee species recorded in the county up to the end of 2016 have a species account, each with a description of the female and male based on unfaded specimens. The species accounts focus on the adult stage of each bee, but of course this is only one part of the life cycle. The descriptions refer to features visible in the field or in photographs. Also provided are notes on flight season, distribution, habitat, flowers visited, nesting and parasites observed. Notes on parasites focus largely on cleptoparasites (cuckoos). Information in the species accounts apply to Norfolk observations except where indicated as coming from another source such as the Bees, Wasps and Ants Recording Society (BWARS) or other authors. The initials of recorders are given where new or unusual observations are made. Images were taken by the author in Norfolk unless otherwise indicated by photographer's initials in [ ].

IDENTIFYING BEES

As mentioned in the Introduction, this is not intended to be a comprehensive identification guide. Bee identification often requires the use of microscopic features using keys. However, in many cases it is possible to track down a bee to a particular species from an image, especially if the bee is fresh and unfaded. The starting point for those new to bees is to look at the spread of bee genera on page 35. Familiarisation with these is the first step to knowing bees well. It is important to look at the hind legs first of all to see if these have a true pollen basket, because the most likely identification will be a Honeybee.

Having picked out a genus which seems to match your bee, go to the relevant genus account indicated. It is worth looking first at the common species in the genus with plenty of records on the map and which emerge at the right time of year. By reading the descriptions and notes and comparing with the images in the book a decision might be reached. As with all species, there are field characteristics which help with identification, and these are sometimes very different from the features listed in keys. Eye colour can be useful but does not last when a bee is dead. Flight patterns, flowers visited and nesting behaviour are features to notice and you will soon be able to identify some bees as they move from flower to flower or build their nests. The hope is that the reader will be amazed by the variety and beauty of Norfolk's bees and become familiar with the main groups, where and when to see them and how they behave. With luck some people will be inspired go on to study bees in more depth, perhaps starting with bees in the garden, and be able submit records to the county recorder.

Males and females Females often have pollen collecting hairs on their body but males do not. Cleptoparasitic bees and *Hylaeus* species have no pollen collecting hairs in either sex. Males generally emerge a week or more before females. Size is very variable even within a species, depending on the amount of food available to the larva and the presence of parasites. Males average smaller than females in most bee species but *Anthidium* males are larger than females. Females have shorter

Honeybee on bluebell with a ball of moistened pollen in the pollen basket. Notice also the long marginal cell at the front edge of the forewing, extending nearly to the tip

Megachile leachella ♂ showing green eyes, June

antennae than males with 12 segments as opposed to 13 in males. Females have six visible segments on the 'abdomen' (strictly called the 'gaster') while males have seven. Females have a sting whereas males do not. Males of some species have more brightly coloured eyes.

Carrying pollen Female foraging bees carry pollen back to the nest using pollen hairs called a scopa. The scopa may be under the abdomen as in *Chelostoma*, *Heriades*, *Hoplitis*, *Megachile* and *Osmia* or on the hind legs as in *Andrena*, *Anthidium*, *Anthophora*, *Apis*, *Bombus*, *Colletes*, *Dasypoda*, *Eucera*, *Halictus*, *Lasioglossum*, *Macropis*, *Melitta* and *Panurgus*. *Hylaeus* carry pollen in their crop (they ingest it) and the cuckoo bees *Bombus* (some), *Coelioxys*, *Epeolus*, *Melecta*, *Nomada*, *Sphecodes* and *Stelis* do not carry pollen. Bees which collect pollen from just one genus of plants are termed oligolectic: bees which collect a wide range of pollen are polylectic.

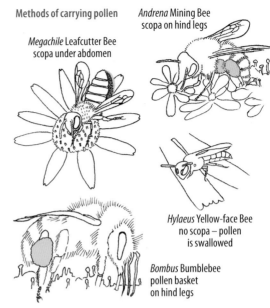

Methods of carrying pollen

Megachile Leafcutter Bee
scopa under abdomen

Andrena Mining Bee
scopa on hind legs

Hylaeus Yellow-face Bee
no scopa – pollen
is swallowed

Bombus Bumblebee
pollen basket
on hind legs

Bee anatomy

Terms used in the species accounts for parts of a bee

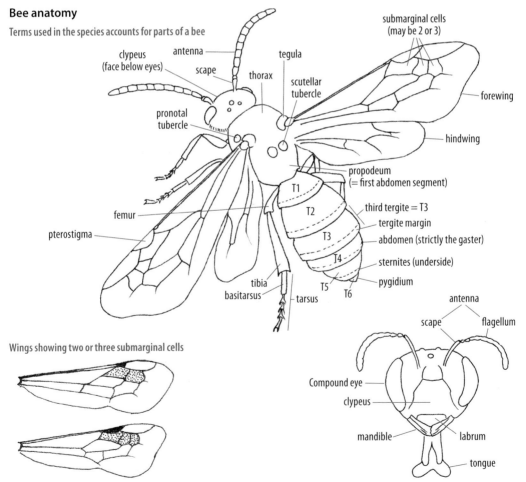

clypeus (face below eyes)
antenna
scape
thorax
tegula
scutellar tubercle
submarginal cells (may be 2 or 3)
forewing
pronotal tubercle
hindwing
propodeum (= first abdomen segment)
T1
T2
femur
third tergite = T3
tergite margin
pterostigma
T3
abdomen (strictly the gaster)
T4
sternites (underside)
tibia
basitarsus
T5 T6
pygidium
tarsus

Wings showing two or three submarginal cells

antenna
scape
flagellum
Compound eye
clypeus
mandible
labrum
tongue

Hoverfly *Eristalis intricarius* ♀, August

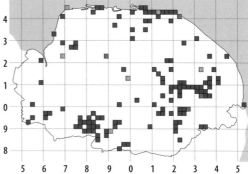

Bee fly *Bombylius major* on grape hyacinth, May

Final check – is it a bee?

Some flies are very good bee mimics so it is important to check that your supposed bee has four wings rather than two. Flies also lack the long antennae of bees. The hoverfly *Eristalis tenax* is a good Honeybee mimic, even letting its legs dangle in flight as if carrying pollen. The hoverflies *Eristalis intricarius*, *Merodon equestris* and *Volucella bombylans* all mimic more than one bumblebee colour pattern. The bee fly *Bombylius major* looks very like an *Anthophora*, but its tongue remains sticking out as it flies.

DISTRIBUTION MAPS

Records used to plot the distribution maps derive from the county recorder Tim Strudwick for 'solitary' bees and David Richmond for bumblebees. Records come from a variety of sources: the Norfolk Biodiversity Information Service (NBIS) at County Hall, the National Biodiversity Network (NBN), collections held at Norwich Castle Museum, published papers, unpublished lists and records submitted by observers. All records are validated so far as possible by the county recorders. The author has inspected aculeate collections at Norwich, Cambridge and the Natural History Museum, London. The total number of records was 14,476: 4,819 of them for bumblebees and 4,030 for

Andrena. A large proportion of the records is from the current century, relatively little recording having been done in the 20th century. All the records come from casual recording rather than systematic surveys. The records tend to cluster round the homes of the most active recorders, namely county recorder Tim Strudwick at Brundall, Geoff Nobes near Watton and the author at Weybourne. There have also been several surveys in the Brecks. However an effort has been made to cover less visited areas such as the Fens and parts of West Norfolk. The maps were plotted by the author using DMAP on a tetrad scale (2 × 2 km squares). Three symbols are used representing different time bands: 2000–present (green), 1980–1999 (pink) and pre-1980 (red) (see example map above). These conform to the time bands used by BWARS. Some pre-2000 records based on place names may be displaced by one tetrad owing to uncertainty about the exact locality.

LOOKING FOR BEES

Finding a particular species of bee is a matter of detective work and persistence. To succeed it is necessary to look at the right time of day in the bee's flight season, on the right flowers in the right habitat in good weather conditions. Careful searching is certain to reveal more new species in the coming years. The author is very keen to help anyone with identification and recording in the county.

BEE GENERA

There are 27 genera of bees represented in the British Isles (omitting one doubtful one, *Dufourea*). The images show examples of each genus, 24 of them occurring in Norfolk. *Eucera* has not been seen in the county for many years. *Ceratina* and *Xylocopa* have not yet been recorded in the county but might soon turn up. The number of species of each genus recorded in the county post-2000 is shown in brackets. Note that the sizes of bees are not to scale.

The 27 bee genera – the number of species of each genus recorded in the county post-2000 is shown in brackets. Note that the sizes of bees are not to scale

Andrena (42) p.51

Anthidium (1) p.127

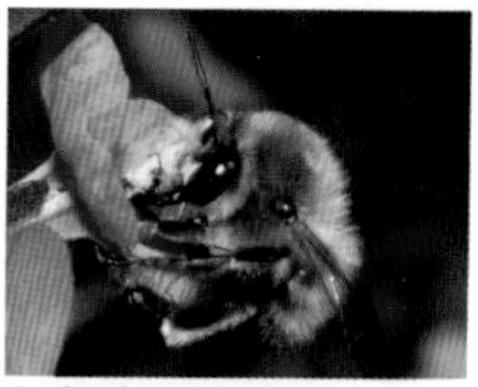

Anthophora (4) p.172

Apis (1) p.200

Bombus (18) p.177

Ceratina (0)

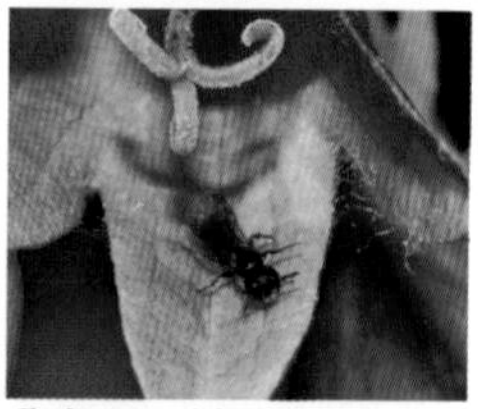

Chelostoma (2) p.131

Coelioxys (4) p.149

Colletes (8) p.36

Dasypoda (1) p.126

Epeolus (2) p.169

Eucera (0) p.171

Halictus (3) p.92

Heriades (1) p.130

Hoplitis (1) p.140

Hylaeus (8) p.45

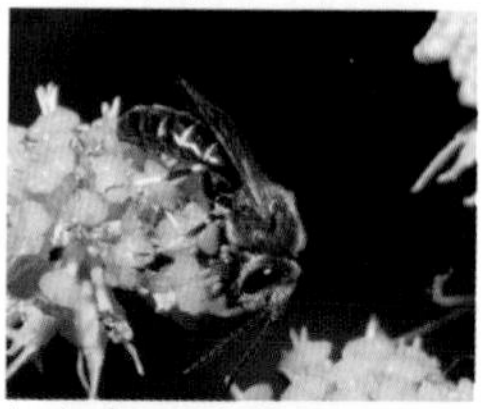

Lasioglossum (23) p.95

Macropis (1) p.125

Megachile (7) p.141

Melecta (1) p.176

Melitta (3) p.121

Nomada (19) p.152

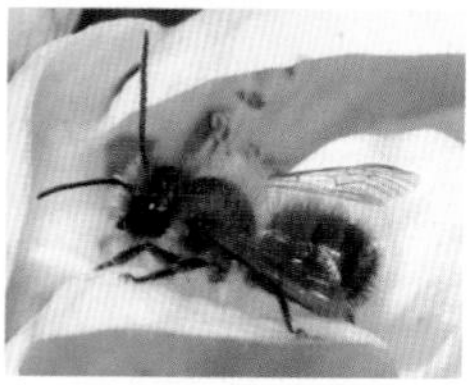

Osmia (6) p.133

Panurgus (2) p.90

Sphecodes (13) p.112

Stelis (3) p.128

Xylocopa (0)

There are nine species in this genus in the British Isles, eight occurring in Norfolk. *Colletes* look superficially like *Andrena*, but differ in having a characteristic curved vein on the forewing and a lobed tongue rather than a pointed one. There are prominent white marginal bands on the tergites of all but one of the Norfolk species. Pollen is collected on the hind legs and under the propodeum. The tongue is used to spread a cellophane-like layer round the nest chamber, which contains a semi-liquid pollen food store.

Colletes succinctus ♀ collecting heather pollen, Beeston Common, 8 September

Several *Colletes* species nest in aggregations sometimes numbering in the hundreds or thousands. Nests are made in the ground and are often attended by cleptoparasitic bees of the genus *Epeolus*. *Colletes* are generally difficult to separate without microscopic examination. There is a tendency for each species to specialise in a particular pollen source. This and flight season can give a clue to identification. Predators include the wasp *Cerceris rybyensis*.

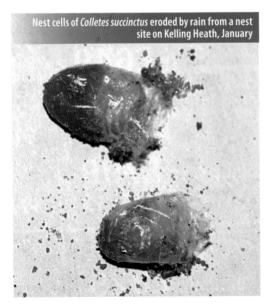
Nest cells of *Colletes succinctus* eroded by rain from a nest site on Kelling Heath, January

Cerceris rybyensis ♀ with a paralysed *C. succinctus*, Weybourne, 16 August

Colletes cunicularius Early Colletes

Females are about the size of a Honeybee with pale brown hairs on the clypeus and thorax. The abdomen lacks the prominent marginal hair bands seen in all other British species of *Colletes* making it relatively easy to identify. **Males** are similar in colour to females but smaller and slimmer.

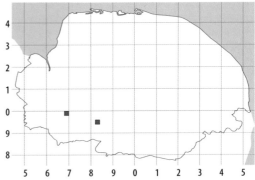

♀ at nest aggregation, Stoke Ferry, 28 April. Females were excavating nest holes on this date but none were yet bringing in pollen

- ■ **FLIGHT** April–May.
- ■ **DISTRIBUTION** This species has historically been largely confined to coastal dunes of Wales, Lancashire and Cumbria, but in recent years colonies have turned up in some southern and midland counties. The species was first seen in Norfolk in 2015 when large nesting aggregations were discovered at Lynford Water (GN) and at Stoke Ferry (TB, NO). From the colony sizes it seems likely that they had been present for several years undiscovered.
- ■ **HABITAT** Sites with willows near suitable nesting areas.
- ■ **FLOWERS VISITED** Oligolectic on willows.
- ■ **NESTING** Both Norfolk nesting sites are in loose sand: the banks of the Cut-off Channel and a worked out sand pit.
- ■ **PARASITES** No cleptoparasitic bees have been recorded in the British Isles.

♀ with willow pollen [TB]

♂, [TB]

Colletes daviesanus Davies' Colletes

Females have pale clypeal hairs and reddish-brown hairs on the head and thorax. There are broad pale marginal bands on the abdomen. Under a microscope, the sparse punctures on T1 are diagnostic. **Males** are similar in colour pattern to females.

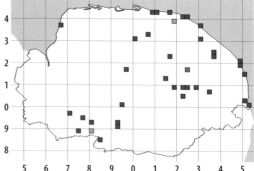

♀ on garden Asteraceae sp. Bromyard, Herefordshire, 17 July

- **FLIGHT** June–September.
- **DISTRIBUTION** Widespread in the county but seemingly avoiding the claylands south of Norwich.
- **HABITAT** Frequent in gardens, including those in Norwich. Less confined to light soils than *Colletes fodiens*.
- **FLOWERS VISITED** Garden *Anthemis*, garden dog daisy, hogweed, scentless mayweed, tansy, yarrow.
- **NESTING** Often nests in aggregations. Sites recorded include lime mortar of a wall (Briston), cliffs (Gorleston), root plates (Hoe Rough, Marsham Heath, Sutton Fen) and a sand face (Snettisham Common).
- **PARASITES** *Epeolus variegatus* (BWARS).

♂ Bromyard, Herefordshire, 17 July

Colletes fodiens Hairy-saddled Colletes

Females have pale clypeal hairs and bright reddish brown hair on the thorax. There are broad white marginal bands on the abdomen. T1 is more hairy with denser punctures than in *Colletes daviesanus*, but they are difficult to separate in the field. **Males** are similar in colour pattern to females.

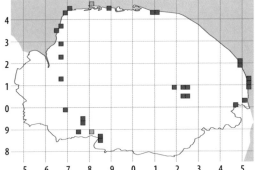

♀, Weybourne Camp, 30 July

- ■ **FLIGHT** July–September.
- ■ **DISTRIBUTION** Confined to light soils on the coast, around Norwich, in west Norfolk and in the Brecks. Recorded at Snettisham, Scolt Head, Weybourne Camp and on the dunes from Winterton southwards but apparently absent from the soft cliffs between Weybourne and Happisburgh, perhaps because they are north-east facing and receive too little sun.
- ■ **HABITAT** Sandy soils with abundant ragwort.
- ■ **FLOWERS VISITED** Bramble, creeping thistle, field scabious, heather (ling), hebe, hogweed, ragwort, tansy, yarrow.
- ■ **NESTING** Not observed in Norfolk. Does not form large nesting aggregations (SF).
- ■ **PARASITES** *Epeolus* sp. (BWARS).

♂ on ragwort, Stoke Ferry, 16 July

Colletes halophilus Sea Aster Bee

Females are large with pale hairs on the clypeus and vivid orange-red hair on the top of the head and thorax. The broad marginal bands on the tergites have a slightly orange tint. **Males** have pale buff-brown hair on the clypeus and thorax.

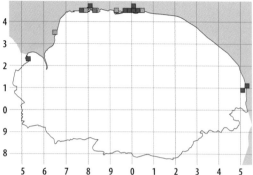

Mating pair, Blakeney Point, 28 August

- **FLIGHT** August–October.
- **DISTRIBUTION** The main populations are at Morston, Blakeney, Blakeney Point, Stiffkey, Scolt Head and Breydon Water/Great Yarmouth North Denes, with further records from Titchwell and pre-2000 records from Wells East Hills and Snettisham/Wolferton. In 1996 there was a large aggregation beside Cley North Hide (PY) but this has since been washed away by storm tides. In August 2016 a male was recorded near Terrington St Clement, 3 km from the saltmarsh. There are probably populations west of King's Lynn.
- **HABITAT** Saltmarshes and sand dunes.
- **FLOWERS VISITED** Pollen is taken largely from sea aster. Also recorded on sea-lavender, ragwort, sea rocket, sheep's-bit and stork's-bill.
- **NESTING** Forms very large nesting aggregations. These can be on the edges of creeks or in sand dunes with a sparse covering of grass. On Scolt Head Field and Foster describe a nest site at Butcher's Beach on shingle in eroded dunes with scattered plants which could be covered by the highest spring tides. The aggregations can cover many square metres, and at Stiffkey one is reported to stretch for 50 m along the sides of a creek. Nests can apparently survive inundation.
- **PARASITES** *Epeolus variegatus* recorded at nest aggregation, Breydon Water e.g. 7 September 2014 (TS).

♂s attempting to mate with one ♀, Blakeney Point, 28 August

Colletes hederae Ivy Bee

Females are up to 15 mm in length. The orange tint to the marginal bands is characteristic, though *Colletes halophilus* can show similar colouration. **Males** have whiter marginal bands.

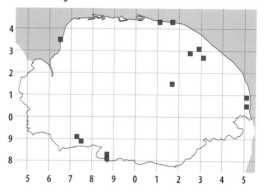

♀, Weybourne, 14 October

- **FLIGHT** September–November.
- **DISTRIBUTION** First recorded in Norfolk in October 2013 at Snettisham (TI). In 2014 it appeared at Morston (nesting), Weybourne and Sheringham and in 2015 at Great Yarmouth and in the Brecks. In 2016 several nesting aggregations were found. There are now probably many more locations than shown on the map.
- **HABITAT** Anywhere there is ivy and suitable nest sites.
- **FLOWERS VISITED** Ivy, prickly sowthistle, ragwort (males).
- **NESTING** Nesting at the same site as *Colletes halophilus* (which had finished nesting) on 29 September 2015 on a road embankment near Gorleston. A nest aggregation was present in a newly created 'bee bank' on Beeston Common in September 2016. Males were first seen on 9 September. 80–100 nest holes were present on 20 September. A nest aggregation containing 3,000–5,000 bees was present at Queens Hills, Costessey in September 2016 (TS) with a further small aggregation at Felmingham (TH).
- **PARASITES** *Epeolus cruciger* (BWARS).

♂, Beaune, France, September

♀ at nest site, Beeston Common, 20 September

♂s competing for a newly emerged ♀, Dry Sandford Pit, Oxfordshire, October [PC]

Colletes marginatus Margined Colletes

The smallest British *Colletes*. **Females**: the sparse, short hair on the face and thorax allows the cuticle to shine through, giving a dull appearance. The anterior of T1 has a covering of long hair and T2–T4 have prominent white marginal bands. **Males** have a similar colour pattern to females.

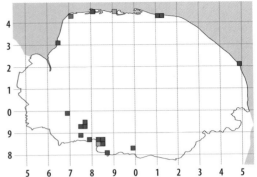

♀ on wild mignonette, Weybourne, 4 August

- **FLIGHT** June-August.
- **DISTRIBUTION** Generally a coastal species nationally with the only British inland records occurring in the Brecks, where it is widespread as far west as Stoke Ferry. On the coast it has been recorded at Scolt Head, Weybourne and Winterton post-2000 and at Holme Dunes 1970 and Wells 1982.
- **HABITAT** Coastal dunes and cliffs. Inland it is associated with sandy areas.
- **FLOWERS VISITED** Polylectic and not strongly associated with Asteraceae unlike other small *Colletes*, but has been recorded on ragwort. Females observed on sea holly at Scolt Head (AM) and on wild mignonette at Weybourne and the Brecks.
- **NESTING** No nest sites observed in Norfolk. Nests in small aggregations (BWARS).
- **PARASITES** *Epeolus cruciger* (BWARS).

♀, Weybourne, 4 August

Colletes similis Bare-saddled Colletes

Females have pale hairs around the antennae but the clypeus has very sparse hair. There is reddish hair on the thorax. The first tergite is bare apart from tufts of hair at the forward margins. The pale band on the hind margin of the first tergite is interrupted in the middle. **Males** have a similar colour pattern.

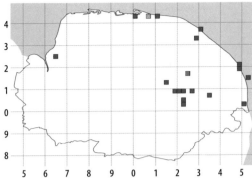

♀ (faded) on tansy, Weybourne, 12 August

- ■ **FLIGHT** June–September.
- ■ **DISTRIBUTION** Recorded on the north and east coasts, around Norwich, the Brecks (though apparently not post-2000 and not on the Norfolk side) and from Ling Common in the west.
- ■ **HABITAT** Prefers light soils and has a similar distribution to *Colletes fodiens*, but not so closely linked to sandy sites as that species (BWARS).
- ■ **FLOWERS VISITED** Recorded on wild mignonette, ragwort, tansy. Generally specialises in Asteraceae.
- ■ **NESTING** No nest sites observed in Norfolk.
- ■ **PARASITES** *Epeolus variegatus* (BWARS).

♀ (faded), Weybourne, 12 August

Colletes succinctus Heather Colletes

A medium sized species. **Females** have pale hairs on the clypeus and orange hairs on the head and thorax. The bands on the tergites are white with an orange tint and an orange transparent band of cuticle on the margin of T1 (also seen in *Colletes halophilus* and *Colletes hederae*). **Males** resemble females in colour pattern.

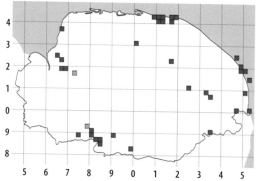

♀ on heather, Swanton Novers Great Wood, 16 August

- **FLIGHT** August–October.
- **DISTRIBUTION** Known from Mousehold since the 1860s. Found wherever there is heather, but also occurs on sites some distance from heather. Locally abundant on the western heaths, the Cromer Ridge, the east coast and the Brecks.
- **HABITAT** Heathland, sandy cliffs and coastal dunes, gardens.
- **FLOWERS VISITED** Strongly associated with heather (ling). It also visits garden heathers. Ivy and Asteraceae pollen are also used. Males also recorded on bramble, fennel, hemp-agrimony, thrift, wild mignonette.
- **NESTING** Can nest in large aggregations, for example on Weybourne Cliffs, where thousands of nest holes occur both on a cliff face (which gets the morning sun) and on the flat cliff top. In mid-August 2015 around 2,000 males were swarming on the cliffs and females were beginning to dig nest holes. During the second half of August and early September, females were bringing heather pollen from Kelling Heath, 1.5 km distant. By 10 September the Heather flowers had largely dried up and the bees switched to collecting ivy pollen.
- **PARASITES** Nest sites are commonly attended by the cleptoparasiticc bee *Epeolus cruciger* and sometimes by the cleptoparasitic fly *Miltogramma punctata*. Adults are predated by the wasp *Cerceris rybyensis*.

♂ on heather, Beeston Regis Heath, 8 September

These are very small black bees with pale markings and very little body hair. Males of most species have largely white faces and females usually have two white facial spots or triangles. Most have additional pale body markings. Pollen is ingested and carried in the crop to the nest. Nests are often in plant stems or holes in dead wood, but can be in the ground. The nest is lined with a waterproof secretion, spread by the bi-lobed tongue, as in *Colletes*. The pattern of facial and body markings often allows identification from images. Most species first appear in May. Twelve species occur in the British Isles with nine in Norfolk, eight post-2000.

Hylaeus signatus ♂ on weld,
Dry Sandford Pit, Oxfordshire, 21 June [PC]

Hylaeus communis ♀ Swanton Novers Great Wood, 29 July

Hylaeus brevicornis Short-horned Yellow-face Bee

Females of this small species have a round face with a small oval pale spot (sometimes absent) touching each eye. The body is otherwise black except for a pale spot on the tegulae. There is a pale marking on the upper hind tibiae and a smaller one on the mid and fore tibiae. **Males** have entirely white faces with white markings extending above the antennae on each side. The scapes of the antennae are inflated and black and the thorax and abdomen are also black. The upper mid and hind tibiae and the mid and hind basitarsi are white. The tibiae of the front legs are partly yellow.

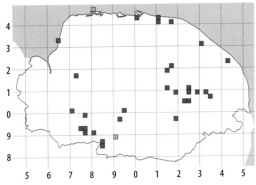

- **FLIGHT** May–September.
- **DISTRIBUTION** Widespread in the county.
- **HABITAT** Woods, fens, brownfield sites, quarries, commons, gardens.
- **FLOWERS VISITED** Bramble, wild carrot, hogweed, wild mignonette, thistles.

- **NESTING** Often nests in bramble stems (TS).
- **PARASITES** The ichneumon *Perithous divinator* emerged from *Hylaeus brevicornis* nests in a bramble twig, Scolt Head.

Hylaeus communis Common Yellow-face Bee

Females have triangular yellow marks on the face, a yellow spot on the tegulae and sometimes yellow pronotal tubercles. There are also pale marks at the top of each tibia (largest on the hind legs). T1 is shiny with sparse punctures and no hair bands. **Males**: the face is largely pale yellow, the yellow extending upwards around the bases of the antennae. The clypeus and supraclypeus are (variably) yellow centrally with black surrounds. The body is black but parts of the tibiae and basitarsi are pale.

- **FLIGHT** May–September.
- **DISTRIBUTION** Widespread and common.
- **HABITAT** Gardens, woodland, commons, Brecks, river valleys.
- **FLOWERS VISITED** Marsh bedstraw, bramble, wild carrot, cow parsley, fennel, garden sea holly, goldenrod, harebell, hebe, shrubby hawkweed, hogweed, mayweed, ivy, hedge parsley, creeping thistle, yarrow.
- **NESTING** Emerged in March from reed stems taken indoors in December (TS).
- **PARASITES** None recorded.

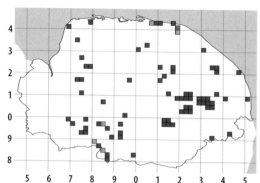

♀ on shrubby hawkweed,
Swanton Novers Great Wood, 28 July

♂ on mayweed, Massingham, 30 July

Hylaeus confusus White-jawed Yellow-face Bee

This species is very similar to *Hylaeus hyalinatus*. **Females**: there are small pale yellow triangular markings adjacent to each eye. The head is broader and shorter than *H. hyalinatus*. The pronotal collar (behind the head) has a pair of whitish stripes and the pronotal tubercles and tegulae are also pale. The basal ends of the tibiae are whitish. **Males**: the face is entirely pale and there is a pale stripe on the antennal scapes. The mandibles have a pale mark but the labrum is black. The tegulae and pronotal tubercles are also pale as are the bases of the tibiae and the mid and hind basitarsi.

- **FLIGHT** May–August.
- **DISTRIBUTION** Widely scattered records, mostly in the south of the county with no records from the coast.
- **HABITAT** Fens, quarries, gardens, Brecks.
- **FLOWERS VISITED** Bramble, hogweed.
- **NESTING** Observed around a sand pit at Strumpshaw Fen (TS).
- **PARASITES** None recorded.

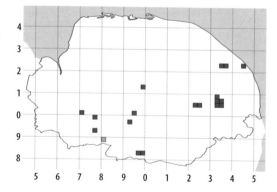

Hylaeus cornutus Spined Hylaeus

Females have a black face with projections surrounding a central depression, thought at one time to be used for carrying pollen, but this is now in doubt (JE). The body and legs are entirely dark apart from the bases of the hind tibiae. **Males** have a black face and yellow antennae, yellow tarsi and partly yellow tibiae (BWARS).

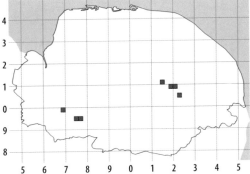

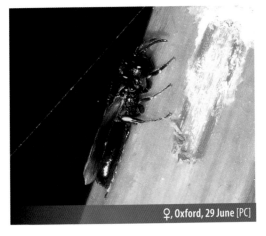

♀, Oxford, 29 June [PC]

- **FLIGHT** June–August.
- **DISTRIBUTION** Recorded in the Norwich area and the Brecks.
- **HABITAT** Grassland in the Wensum Valley in Norwich, brownfield site grassland south and west of the city (TS) and Brecks grassland at Cranwich and Wretton (GN and TS).
- **FLOWERS VISITED** Wild carrot, hogweed.
- **NESTING** No records.
- **PARASITES** None recorded.

Hylaeus dilatatus Chalk Yellow-face Bee

Females have a broad face with a pair of roundish pale patches on the clypeus, not touching the eye margins. There are pale marks on the pronotal collar (sometimes reduced), pale pronotal tubercles and sometimes a pale mark on the tegula. The bases of the tibiae are pale. The abdomen has no hair bands. **Males** have very inflated antennal scapes which are half white and half black above and hollow underneath like a sea shell. The mandibles are white. The thorax is marked similarly to females. The tarsi are white as are the basal parts of the tibiae.

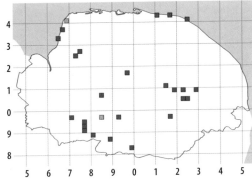

♀ on bramble, Beeston Common, 26 July

- **FLIGHT** June–September.
- **DISTRIBUTION** Widespread and fairly common.
- **HABITAT** Commons, Brecks grassland, brownfield sites, cliffs, chalk grassland.
- **FLOWERS VISITED** Angelica, hogweed, scentless mayweed, wild carrot.
- **NESTING** No records.
- **PARASITES** None recorded.

Hylaeus hyalinatus Hairy Yellow-face Bee

Females have a long narrow head with large triangular pale markings alongside each eye. The antennae are orange beneath. The pronotal collar, pronotal tubercles and tegulae are pale as are the upper ends of the tibiae. There is a fringe of hair at the edge of T1. **Males** have a white face bearing long white hairs (not seen in any other *Hylaeus* species). The tarsi and parts of the tibiae are pale.

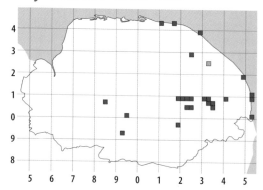

♀, Cambridge, 27 July

- **FLIGHT** May–August.
- **DISTRIBUTION** Frequent but few records in the north or west of the county.
- **HABITAT** Brownfield sites, gardens, churchyards, coastal sites.
- **FLOWERS VISITED** Bramble, cat's-ear, fennel, hebe, hogweed, garden sea holly, oxeye daisy, biting stonecrop, wild carrot, yarrow.
- **NESTING** Observed at holes in house wall and in an oak block, but also seen on bare sand (TS).

♂ on biting stonecrop, Cambridge, 25 June

♂, Oxford, 29 June [PC]

Hylaeus pectoralis Reed Yellow-face Bee

Females are similar to *Hylaeus communis* females but larger with more prominent pale pronotal tubercles. **Males** have a yellow face, pronotal tubercles, upper tibiae and basitarsi (SF).

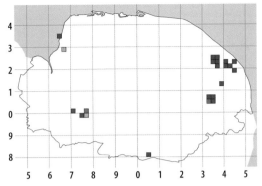

♀, Coryton, Essex, 2015 [SF]

♂, Coryton, Essex, 2015 [SF]

- ■ **FLIGHT** May–August.
- ■ **DISTRIBUTION** Recorded from wetlands in the Broads, Yare valley, Waveney Valley, Foulden Common and Dersingham Bog.
- ■ **HABITAT** Wetlands with reed beds, but not so far recorded on the north coast or the Fens.

- ■ **FLOWERS VISITED** Bramble, cowbane, hogweed, creeping thistle.
- ■ **NESTING** Nests are made in the stems of common reed or in the vacated cigar galls made by *Lipara* flies in these reeds (BWARS).
- ■ **PARASITES** None recorded.

Hylaeus pictipes Little Yellow-face Bee

Females have oblique pale facial markings, pale pronotal tubercles and tegulae and pale bases to the tibiae. **Males** have a white face and narrow antennal scapes. The pronotal collar, tegulae and pronotal tubercles are yellow as are large parts of the tibiae and the tarsi (SF).

- ■ **FLIGHT** June–August (BWARS).
- ■ **DISTRIBUTION** A single record from Norwich by Bridgman in the late 1800s.
- ■ **HABITAT** Woodlands, fens, coastal habitats and gardens (BWARS).
- ■ **FLOWERS VISITED** No records.
- ■ **NESTING** No records.
- ■ **PARASITES** No records.

Hylaeus signatus Large Yellow-face Bee

Females of this large species are bulky looking and dark with small triangular yellow markings on the face. There are yellow marks on the pronotal collar and tegulae and the legs are entirely black. There are hair bands on the sides of T1–T4. **Males** have a very white face but are otherwise dark with similar abdominal hair bands to females.

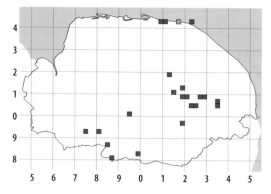

♀ on weld, Weybourne, 25 August

- **FLIGHT** May–August.
- **DISTRIBUTION** Most records are from the Norwich area with scattered records in the south of the county and along the Cromer Ridge.
- **HABITAT** Commons, disturbed ground and brownfield sites with sandy soils where weld or wild mignonette grow.
- **FLOWERS VISITED** Resedaceae: weld and wild mignonette.
- **NESTING** No records.
- **PARASITES** None recorded.

♂ on weld, Weybourne, 25 August

♂'s on wild mignonette, Dry Sandford Pit, Oxfordshire, 21 June [PC]

Forty-seven *Andrena* species have been recorded in Norfolk, of which 42 have been seen post-2000. Three of these 42 species colonised the county since about the year 2000. The term 'mining bee' describes their habit of making nest holes in the ground. These often have a characteristic volcano of soil around the entrance and some species nest in aggregations. Pollen is carried by hairs on the hind legs and also within curved hairs under the propodeum. Some *Andrena* species collect pollen from just one plant type, such as willows or scabious, whereas others use a wide range of pollen sources. A female may take pollen from several species in one pollen load. The short tongue generally limits *Andrena* bees to flowers with a short corolla as a nectar source. The time of year a bee is seen and the flowers it visits can often assist with identification. See also Appendix 1, p.211.

Andrena thoracica second brood ♀ at nest site, Kelling Heath, 28 July

Andrena humilis at nest entrance (above) and approaching with a pollen load (below), Weybourne, May

Andrena humilis nest aggregation during the day (above) and at 10 pm with the bees inside and entrances closed (below)

Andrena alfkenella Alfken's Mini-miner

Females differ from the very similar and much commoner *Andrena minutula* in having punctures on T2 and T3, and the wing stigma is brown rather than black. The body hairs are white, including pale bands on the sides of the tergite margins, similar to those in *A. minutula*. **Males** are also distinguishable from *A. minutula* on the basis of clearer punctures on the tergites, though male *A. minutula* can be somewhat punctured. These details require microscopic examination.

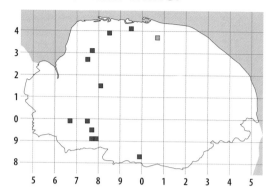

- **FLIGHT** Two brooded: a male was recorded in west Norfolk on 10 April 2014, with all other county records occurring in July or August (latest record three females on 31 August so probably extending into September).
- **DISTRIBUTION** Scarce; recorded in the Brecks, banks of the Cut-off Channel (sandy chalk), Warham Camp, North Creake and chalk grassland in the Sandringham area.
- **HABITAT** Associated with chalk grassland. Males seen swarming round wild parsnip, 23 July 2014.

- **FLOWERS VISITED** Pollen loads from Flitcham included geranium, hogweed, mayweed, red campion and sowthistle (TW).
- **NESTING** No records.
- **PARASITES** No information.

Andrena angustior Groove-faced Mining Bee

Females have a mixture of dark and pale hairs on the clypeus, with some dark hairs between the antennae and the thorax has reddish brown hair. Tibia hairs are pale and there are indistinct pale marginal hair bands on the abdomen. T5 and T6 have black hair. Both sexes have wide marginal areas on the abdomen. **Males** have long overlapping mandibles but without a flange at the base. The clypeus has pale hairs and there are some black hairs along the margins of the eyes. The abdomen has sparse long pale hairs, longest on tergites 1–3, and the marginal areas are shiny.

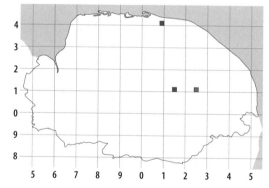

♀ on creeping buttercup, Kelling Heath, 24 May

- **FLIGHT** May–June.
- **DISTRIBUTION** It was recorded on Mousehold Heath in 1873, but with no further county records until it was discovered on Kelling Heath in May 2012, where a population appeared near the car park (NO). A female was recorded at Costessey in June 2015 (TS).
- **HABITAT** Heathland with scattered shrubs of rowan, gorse, birch and hawthorn.
- **FLOWERS VISITED** Creeping buttercup.
- **NESTING** Female observed entering a hole amongst loose bracken litter on Kelling Heath.
- **PARASITES** *Nomada fabriciana* (BWARS).

Andrena argentata Small Sandpit Mining Bee

Females have pale brown hair on the clypeus and thorax. There are narrow well defined white hair bands on the margins of the tergites. The tibial hairs are pale but with blackish hairs near the junction with the femur. **Males** have a similar colour pattern to females.

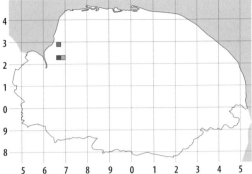

- **FLIGHT** Late July–September.
- **DISTRIBUTION** E A Atmore reports in *Transactions* 1909 "King's Lynn: abundant but very local. There are large colonies in a few restricted spots". There are three female and three male specimens in the University Museum of Zoology, Cambridge from Sandringham Warren 11 August 1954 (PY). The only other record from the 20th century was of a male at Roydon Common in the 1990s (MA). The species was rediscovered at Roydon Common on 26 August 2016 when a small nesting aggregation was found on a path, with further females bringing pollen loads to parts of the main track (TB, NO). It seems likely that the bee has been present throughout but overlooked. This is the most northerly known extant site in the British Isles.
- **HABITAT** Heathland with open loose sand.
- **FLOWERS VISITED** Heather (ling).
- **NESTING** Nests in aggregations in loose sand. The bees can burrow through collapsing sand as they enter their nest hole.
- **PARASITES** *Nomada baccata*.

♀ on heather, Roydon Common, 26 August

♀, Roydon Common, 26 August

Andrena barbilabris Sandpit Mining Bee

Females have pale clypeal hairs and rich brown hair on the thorax. The tibial hairs are blackish and the abdomen has narrow interrupted white bands. **Males** look fluffy with long whitish hairs on the face, including a fringe of white hairs hanging over the mandibles. There are a few black hairs along the margins of the eyes. The abdomen is narrow with interrupted white hair bands on the margins, and the legs are black.

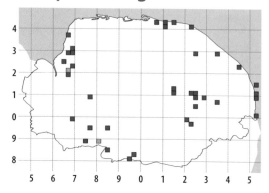

- **FLIGHT** April–June.
- **DISTRIBUTION** Widespread in sandy places in warm microhabitats.
- **HABITAT** Found on heathland, coastal sites, railway banks, river banks and sandy paths. Colonies sometimes number in the hundreds. Nests are usually made in loose sand, where the nest burrows can collapse on departure. Returning females burrowing for their nest entrances are often pounced upon by males, which attempt to mate, even when the female has a pollen load. These females usually buzz and try to shake them off, but the males sometimes pursue them down their burrows.
- **FLOWERS VISITED** Polylectic including willows.
- **NESTING** Nests in aggregations on level or slightly sloping bare sandy ground such as the sides of tracks and pathways. Males patrol low along the edges of vegetation and bask on bare ground.
- **PARASITES** *Sphecodes pellucidus* is usually present at nest aggregations of *Andrena barbilabris* and is one of the few *Sphecodes* species to parasitise an *Andrena*. *S. reticulatus* may also be a parasite (BWARS).

♀ with pollen load, Kelling Heath, 18 May. She is covered in sand grains from burrowing

♂ Kelling Heath, 2 May

Andrena bicolor Gwynne's Mining Bee

Females have black hairs on the clypeus and the abdomen bears rich red brown hair. The hind femur and tibia have long yellowish-orange hairs. There are black hairs on all other leg parts, beneath the wings and at the tip of the abdomen. The tergites have pale, poorly defined, marginal hair bands. Summer brood females have paler hair beneath the wings and between the antennae. **Males** are usually rather small and thin, with bushy black hairs on the clypeus. There are indistinct pale hair bands at the edges of the tergites.

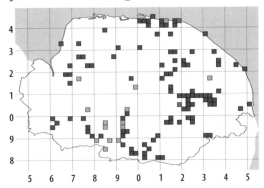

- **FLIGHT** March–August in two broods.
- **DISTRIBUTION** One of the commonest early spring *Andrena* species. On 9 March 2014 hundreds of *A. bicolor* were flying in Swanton Novers woods. This was the first warm day of the year, with temperatures reaching 19°C. Males and females were present in about equal numbers but at this stage none of the females was carrying pollen.
- **HABITAT** Woodland rides, gardens, waysides, field margins, scrub.
- **FLOWERS VISITED** Angelica, apple, bramble, lesser celandine, dandelion, gorse, hedge parsley, hogweed, lesser trefoil, primrose, willows, tormentil, wild parsnip, white bryony. Pollen loads from Swanton Novers included sowthistle and tormentil (TW).
- **NESTING** Observed entering nest holes in a sloping bank beside Weybourne beach in compacted glacial material, and several females occupied a purpose made bank made of gravelly substrate on Beeston Common. Nesting also seen at Walsey Hills in gravelly slightly sloping ground.
- **PARASITES** *Nomada fabriciana* (BWARS).

♀ at nest site, Beeston Common, 14 March

♀ with pollen, Weybourne, 23 March

♂, Walsey Hills, 17 April

Andrena bimaculata Large Gorse Mining Bee

This species was divided into three in Bridgman's 19th century collection in the Norwich Castle Museum as *Andrena bimaculata*, *A. decorata* and *A. vitrea*, but it was later recognised that these three represented just one species, with slight differences between first and second broods. **Females** have mixed dark and pale clypeal hairs. The hairs on the thorax and tibia are pale and there are pale hair fringes to the margins of the tergites. Some individuals have red markings on the first two tergites of the abdomen, giving the species its name. **Males** have long black hairs on the clypeus and round the antennae, with some brown hairs on top of the head. There are long brown hairs on the thorax. The abdomen has pale marginal hair bands with black hairs on the last two segments. Some males have a reddish margin to T1 and T2.

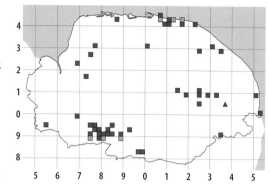

- **FLIGHT** Two broods: early April–June and July–August.
- **DISTRIBUTION** Found especially on heathland, sandy soils around Norwich and near the coast. It is close to the northern edge of its range in Norfolk. Bridgman in his 1876 NNNS Presidential Address, noted that *Andrena bimaculata* "literally swarmed, not only on Mousehold, but all around Norwich".
- **HABITAT** Sandy soils, heathland.
- **FLOWERS VISITED** Alexanders, blackthorn, bramble, gorse, hogweed, knapweed, willows, white bryony. A pollen load from Weybourne contained willow pollen (TW).
- **NESTING** Bridgman reports nests of 20 females on Mousehold 2 April 1876 "generally dispersed over the bare loamy spots. They do not burrow very deeply and generally the mouth of the burrow was at the root of a tuft of grass, and partially concealed by it". Nesting was observed in bare ground of an artificial bee bank, Kelling Heath August 2016.
- **PARASITES** *Nomada fulvicornis* (BWARS).

Second brood ♀, red form on bramble, Kelling Heath, 13 July

♂, Kelling Heath, 23 March

♂, Salisbury Plain, July

Andrena chrysosceles Hawthorn Mining Bee

Females have pale hairs on the clypeus and sparse brown hair on the thorax. The hind tibiae are red as are the tarsi on all legs. The hairs on the legs are pale. There are narrow white marginal hair bands on the abdomen and reddish hairs at the tip. The wings can look yellowish. **Males** have a cream patch on the face. All tibiae are red together with the terminal part of the hind tarsus. The abdomen has diffuse white marginal hair bands. There are pale reddish hairs on the tip of the abdomen.

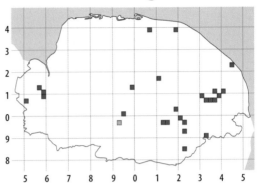

- **FLIGHT** March–June.
- **DISTRIBUTION** Widely scattered records in the county, but probably under-recorded.
- **HABITAT** Parkland, woodland clearings, churchyards.
- **FLOWERS VISITED** Bramble: known to be polylectic.
- **NESTING** No records.
- **PARASITES** A stylopised male from Emneth Hungate 2012 had a much reduced white face patch. A stylopised female was also collected in the county. *Nomada fabriciana* is a cleptoparasite (BWARS).

♀, Wiggenhall St Mary, 12 May

♂, Derbyshire, 6 May

Mating pair, Bernwood Forest, Buckinghamshire, 25 April [PC]

Andrena cineraria Ashy Mining Bee

Females are unmistakable, being generally black, with grey/white hair bands on the collar and scutellum and white hairs on the clypeus.
Males have long white hair on the clypeus and thorax. The abdomen is black and shining with white hair tufts at the sides of each tergite.

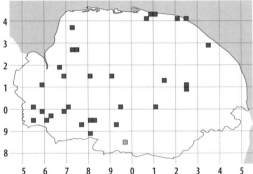

♀, Kelling Heath, 27 April

- **FLIGHT** April–June.
- **DISTRIBUTION** There is only one pre-2000 record for Norfolk: 1997, West Harling (KD), but it is now widespread in the county often with large nesting aggregations. It is well established in the Fens where it uses willows.
- **HABITAT** Woodland, gardens and parkland.
- **FLOWERS VISITED** Alexanders, gorse and willows.
- **NESTING** Nesting aggregations were found in short, hard-packed grassland on chalk, including Caste Acre and Flitcham and also on raised banks in the Fens.
- **PARASITES** A female loaded with pollen attracted a shadow fly (*Leucophora* sp.) on Kelling Heath, May 2015 (AMg). *Nomada lathburiana* and *N. goodeniana* (BWARS).

♂ on willow, Ten Mile Bank, the Fens, 11 April

Andrena clarkella Clarke's Mining Bee

Females have black hairs on the clypeus, golden brown hair on the upper thorax, grading to black beneath. The hind tibia and tarsus are translucent orange, bearing golden brown hairs, but all other leg parts have black hair. The abdomen has a covering of black hairs with indistinct paler marginal bands. **Males** have pale hairs on the clypeus, orange brown hair on the thorax and pale marginal bands on the abdomen. The legs are black.

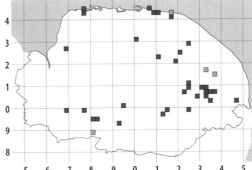

♀, Beeston Common, 19 March

- **FLIGHT** February–April. Bees appear on the first warm days of spring when temperatures reach about 15°C. They appear slightly later than *Andrena bicolor*.
- **DISTRIBUTION** Widespread but thinly distributed.
- **HABITAT** Woodland, scrub, heathland and parkland.
- **FLOWERS VISITED** Willows and possibly hazel.
- **NESTING** Nests in aggregations often on sloping or vertical surfaces such as banks and root plates. They can use woodland sites which become shaded after leaf emergence. Males patrol nest aggregations as well as sunny branches and tree trunks.
- **PARASITES** *Nomada leucophthalma* and shadow fly *Leucophora* sp.

♂ recently emerged at a nest site on Beeston Common, 19 March

Andrena coitana Small Flecked Mining Bee

Females have pale hair on the clypeus and on the thorax. The hind tibia has dark hairs above and white hairs below and the abdomen has interrupted white marginal bands on tergites 2–4. **Males** have a white area on the clypeus and a covering of white hairs on the thorax and legs. The tergites are shiny with prominent marginal bands, slightly narrowed at the centre.

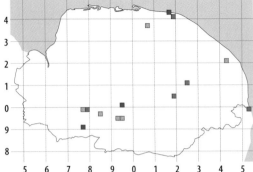

- ■ **FLIGHT** June–July.
- ■ **DISTRIBUTION** Bridgman 1879 says "not uncommon round the city". Wainright 1901 found it to be "very abundant on Ragwort" at West Runton. It was recorded at Beeston Common and Aylmerton in the 1970s and 1980s (KD). Now rare in Norfolk with only three post-2000 records: two in the Brecks and again at Beeston Common (SF). It seems to have declined but may be overlooked.
- ■ **HABITAT** Scrub and heathland.
- ■ **FLOWERS VISITED** Observed on bramble in Wales and France.
- ■ **NESTING** Not observed.
- ■ **PARASITES** *Nomada obtusifrons* (no county records since 19th century).

♀ on bramble, Cornwall [PS]

♂, Le Crotoy, northern France, 4 July

Andrena denticulata Grey-banded Mining Bee

Females have pale hair on the clypeus and long pale hair on the thorax mixed with some dark hairs (distinguishing it from *Andrena flavipes* which has only pale hairs on the thorax). The hind tibia has stiff dark hairs on the upper surface which are shorter than the width of the tibia, and pale hairs below. (The tibial hairs are much shorter than those of *A. flavipes*.) There are prominent white hair bands on the margins of the abdomen. **Males** have pale hair on the clypeus, long curved mandibles and a ridge running behind each eye. There is a mixture of pale and black hairs on the thorax (as in the female) and pale marginal bands on the tergites, less pronounced than those of females.

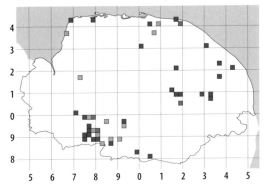

- **FLIGHT** July–September.
- **DISTRIBUTION** Widespread with a good population in the Brecks.
- **HABITAT** Sandy areas with open rough (sometimes wet) ground, including rides in Swanton Novers Great Wood, Beeston Common, the Glaven Valley and Breckland rides.
- **FLOWERS VISITED** Yellow Asteraceae especially ragwort and fleabane. Pollen loads from Beeston Common included bramble, black knapweed and ragwort (TW).
- **NESTING** A female with a pollen load entered a hole on a 'bee bank' dug for aculeates on Beeston Common 27 July 2016.
- **PARASITES** *Nomada rufipes* (DB).

♀ on fleabane, Swanton Novers Great Wood, 27 August

♂ on ragwort, Cranwich, 27 July

Andrena dorsata Short-fringed Mining Bee

Females have pale hair on the clypeus and foxy red brown hair on the upper thorax and scutellum, with white hairs beneath. The hairs on the tibia are pale yellow and relatively short and the floccus hairs are white. The hind tarsus and usually the tip of the hind tibia are orange. The abdomen has distinctive white marginal bands on tergites 2, 3 and 4. **Males** have pale hair on the clypeus but some black hairs along the eye margins. The fourth antennal segment is short (long in *Andrena scotica* male). The thorax hairs are pale and there are white marginal bands at the sides of the tergites, distinct in some individuals but hard to see in others. The hind and mid tarsi are orange.

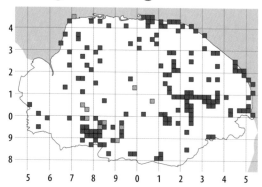

- **FLIGHT** Two broods; April–June and July–September.

♀ Weybourne, April

- **DISTRIBUTION** Widespread and common. North Norfolk is close to the northern edge of its British range.
- **HABITAT** Very varied including hedgerows, gardens, woodland edge and heathland.
- **FLOWERS VISITED** Alexanders, blackthorn, bramble, creeping thistle, gorse, ground-ivy, hedge parsley, hogweed, *Pyracantha*, willow, wild radish, white bryony. A pollen load from Weybourne contained cow parsley and *Sinapis* sp. (TW).
- **NESTING** Nesting in bare sandy ground, Kelling Heath July 2016.
- **PARASITES** No common *Nomada* species seems to be associated on the British mainland. In 2016 *N. zonata* has been found in Kent, whose host is *A. dorsata* in Europe (BWARS). *Sphecodes reticulatus* may be a parasite of the second brood (BWARS). The wasp *Cerceris rybyensis* preys on this species.

♂ on blackthorn, Walsey Hills, 17 April

♀ entering nest hole, Kelling Heath, 28 July

Andrena flavipes Yellow-legged Mining Bee

Females have a mixture of pale and brown hairs on the clypeus, pale hairs on the thorax and long yellow pollen hairs on the tibia. There are prominent broad white marginal bands on the tergites. *Andrena denticulata* is somewhat similar but has much shorter hairs on the tibia. **Males** have mixed pale and brown hairs on the clypeus, pale hairs on the thorax and narrow pale marginal bands on the abdomen.

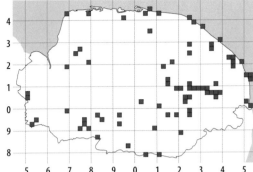

♀ on daisy, Le Crotoy, France, April

- **FLIGHT** Double brooded: April–June and July–September.
- **DISTRIBUTION** The range has expanded from the south of England in recent years. Absent from Norfolk until about 2002, but now widespread.
- **HABITAT** Sandy or clay soils including the Fens and coastal cliffs.
- **FLOWERS VISITED** Blackthorn, bramble, cherry laurel, daisy, dandelion, gorse, heather (ling), willows.
- **NESTING** Nests singly or in aggregations. Nest sites observed on Weybourne beach and on the banks of the Cut-off Channel at Stoke Ferry.
- **PARASITES** *Nomada fucata*, observed by the author with this species at Overstrand cliffs and at Stoke Ferry and present at several other Norfolk sites (TS). Shadow fly *Leucophora* sp. seen to accompany this species at a nest hole at Stoke Ferry.

♀ Weybourne Beach, 23 March

♂ Fotheringhay, Northamptonshire, 30 June

Andrena fucata Painted Mining Bee

Females: the facial hair is pale and the thorax has pale brown hair with paler hairs on the propodeal pollen basket. The abdomen has sparse fluffy hairs with dark hair on the last tergite. The hind tibia has pale hairs and the hind basitarsus is reddish in both sexes. **Males**: the mandibles are long and curved with a flange at the base and the facial hairs are pale. The thorax hairs are sparse and long, of a reddish brown colour. The abdomen is narrow and shiny with just a few longish hairs. The hind tarsus is orange/red. The overall appearance is rather spindly and some males are very small.

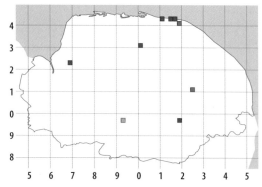

♀ on wild raspberry, Swanton Novers Great Wood, 26 June

♂ covered in holly pollen, Swanton Novers Great Wood, 13 May

- **FLIGHT** May–July.
- **DISTRIBUTION** Found throughout the British Isles but scarce in the county with only about five 20th century records, including north Norfolk, Roydon Common and the Brecks. It was found again in 2012 at Beeston Common, Weybourne and at Swanton Novers Great Wood, where it appears to be reasonably common (NO).
- **HABITAT** Heathland edge, woodland edge, woodland rides.
- **FLOWERS VISITED** Wild raspberry, holly. A specimen from Weybourne in July 2013 had at least six types of very small pollen, including hogweed.
- **NESTING** Not recorded in Norfolk.
- **PARASITES** *Nomada panzeri* (BWARS).

Andrena fulva Tawny Mining Bee

Females are very striking, having entirely black hair on the face, sides of thorax, tip of abdomen and legs, while the rest of the body hair is vivid ginger-brown. **Males**: the clypeus has long white hair, with pale brown hairs around the bases of the antennae and black hairs on the eye margins. The head is large and wide and triangular in profile. The long curved mandibles have a triangular flange at the base. The hair on the thorax is pale orange-brown and the abdomen has brownish marginal bands.

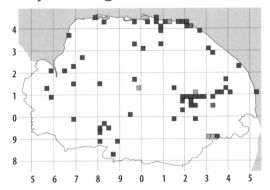

♀ on alexanders, Walsey Hills, 20 April

♂ at nest aggregation, Walsey Hills, 12 April

- **FLIGHT** April–June, with numbers peaking in the second half of April.
- **DISTRIBUTION** Widespread and locally abundant.
- **HABITAT** Gardens, woodland edge, hedgerows, heathland, favouring light soils.
- **FLOWERS VISITED** Polylectic: often seen on blackthorn in April but its activity extends into the flowering period of hawthorn in May. Uses alexanders for pollen and nectar. Also seen on apple and *Pyracantha*.
- **NESTING** Often nests in lawns, sometimes in aggregations, leaving a 'volcano' of earth around the nest holes.
- **PARASITES** *Nomada panzeri* and *N. signata* (BWARS). The latter species is scarce in Norfolk. The bee fly *Bombylius major*.

Andrena fuscipes Heather Mining Bee

Females have pale hair on the clypeus, rufous hairs on the thorax and broad pale marginal hair bands on the abdomen. The hairs on the hind tibia are golden. Care must be taken not to confuse it with *Colletes succinctus*, which is also a heather (ling) specialist. **Males** are slender with longish grey/brown hair and pale marginal bands on the abdomen.

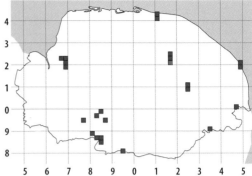

♀ on heather, Kelling Heath, 20 August

♂ (faded) on heather, Kelling Heath, 15 August

- **FLIGHT** Late July–September.
- **DISTRIBUTION** This species is threatened in Europe, the UK being a stronghold because of the abundance of heather (ling). The Norfolk distribution reflects the occurrence of heather in the county. There appears to be a healthy population in the Brecks and west Norfolk with more localised populations on the heathland between Norwich and north Norfolk. It also occurs at Winterton Dunes and Broome Heath.
- **HABITAT** Heathland with bare ground.
- **FLOWERS VISITED** Flowers visited heather (ling) for both pollen and nectar. Bell heather is not used. Heather has very small pollen grains (35μm diameter: Kirk). These adhere to the face of the female bee as she seeks nectar. From time to time the bee pauses to groom this off and passes it to the hind legs. They crawl from flower to flower to quite a large extent but periodically fly to adjacent heather plants.
- **NESTING** Nest sites are scattered among sparse heather, the entrances often partly hidden under the plants. Nest sites are loosely aggregated, perhaps owing to the patchy nature of suitable bare ground. The males patrol open ground, occasionally basking on stones and also take nectar from heather.
- **PARASITES** *Nomada rufipes* parasitises this species. The females can be seen searching among the roots of short growing heather for nest sites.

Andrena haemorrhoa Orange-tailed Mining Bee

Females have pale hair on the clypeus, rich red-brown hair on the thorax and golden hair on the hind tibia. The tibia and tarsus are orange-red. The abdomen has a covering of short white hair and a tuft of orange hair at the tip. **Males** have pale hairs on the clypeus, reddish hairs on the thorax and an orange-red hind tarsus. The hind tibia and mid tarsus are usually partly orange-red. There are also orange hairs on the tip of the abdomen.

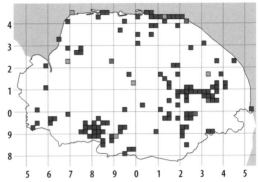

♀ on apple blossom, May

- **FLIGHT** April–June. It was abundant in the Brecks in the second week of April 2015; a bit later on the north coast. Most are finished by late May with a few continuing into June.
- **DISTRIBUTION** Common and widespread. This is one of the most universal and versatile *Andrena* species in Norfolk.
- **HABITAT** Almost all types of habitat including the shingle ridge of Blakeney Point. They can be active when weather conditions are marginal.
- **FLOWERS VISITED** Alexanders, apple, blackthorn, bramble, gorse, hawthorn, hogweed, willows, rowan, sycamore, weld and many others. A pollen load from Kelling Heath contained hawthorn and sycamore (TW).
- **NESTING** Nests are rarely observed in this common species, probably because they are scattered and hidden amongst vegetation. One nest was observed in a lawn in Weybourne. Females loaded with sycamore pollen were seen descending amongst bracken litter with bluebells on Kelling Heath.
- **PARASITES** *Nomada ruficornis* (BWARS).

♀ on apple blossom, May

♂ on forget-me-not, Weybourne, May

Andrena hattorfiana Large Scabious Mining Bee

♂, Weybourne, 9 July

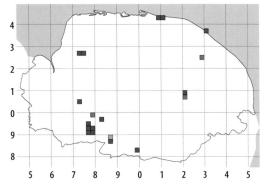

Females are very large and easily identified in the field. They have a strong preference for scabious flowers, the bee typically being laden with pink pollen. There are white hairs on the clypeus and on the thorax and the tibial hairs are yellowish above and white beneath. The abdominal tergites are shiny and largely lacking hairs except for white marginal bands on tergites 3, 4 and 5. There are orange hairs on the final tergite. The wings are suffused with brown. The abdomen can be partly red, but this form has only been recorded once in Norfolk. **Males** are characterised by their white clypeus. The cuticle is otherwise black and the body hairs are white. The tergites are shiny and the wings have a brown tint.

- **FLIGHT** June–August, peaking in the second half of July.
- **DISTRIBUTION** Recorded by Bridgman 1879 at Eaton and Worstead. Currently found in the Brecks, the chalk near Sandringham, the soft cliff coast and at Earlham Cemetery in Norwich where up to 13 females have been recorded (SP).
- **HABITAT** Light soils with good populations of scabious, including arable field margins.
- **FLOWERS VISITED** Field scabious and small scabious.
- **NESTING** No information from Norfolk.
- **PARASITES** *Nomada armata* (not recorded in the county since the 19th century).

♀ on field scabious, Weybourne, 31 July

♀ red form on field scabious, Cranwich Camp, 6 July

Andrena helvola Coppice Mining Bee

Females have pale hair on the clypeus, chestnut brown hair on the thorax and on T1, broad pale marginal bands on T2 and 3 and a less distinct band on T4. The hind tibial hairs are pale and the floccus hairs are white. **Males** have pale clypeus hairs and dark hairs on the eye margins. There are long brown hairs on the thorax and upper abdomen and pale hairs on the final tergite. The middle and hind tibia and tarsus have a pale cuticle.

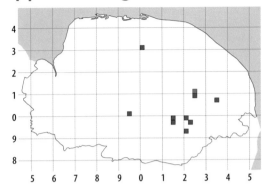

♀ on wood spurge, Parkhill, New Forest, Hampshire, 12 May [PB]

♂ on wood spurge, Rewell Wood, West Sussex, 1 May [PB]

- ■ **FLIGHT** April–June.
- ■ **DISTRIBUTION** Bridgman 1879 found it to be "common in the neighbourhood of the city". Apparently now scarce: recorded from scattered sites.

- ■ **HABITAT** Associated with open wooded sites including Rosary Cemetery in Norwich.
- ■ **FLOWERS VISITED** Hogweed, raspberry.
- ■ **NESTING** Not observed in the county.
- ■ **PARASITES** *Nomada panzeri* (BWARS).

Andrena humilis Buff-tailed Mining Bee

Females are compact bees with a generally ginger appearance. The hind tibia hairs are long and also ginger brown, and there is a longer fringe of hairs on the margin of the T5, which assists in carrying pollen. **Males** have a white patch and white hair on the clypeus, pale hair under the wings and brown hair elsewhere, with pale bands on the tergite margins.

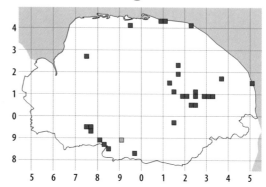

♀ resting on daisy, Weybourne, 21 May

♂, Weybourne, 26 May

- **FLIGHT** Late May–July: females at a nesting aggregation at Weybourne were digging nest holes on 21 May 2015, with a few already collecting pollen. Mating was seen on 22 May. Most of the breeding activity had ended by early June. However, a lone female was bringing pollen to a nest on Kelling Heath on 13 July 2015.
- **DISTRIBUTION** There seem to be two main populations in the county, in the Brecks and in the Norwich area with further sites on the coast.
- **HABITAT** Sandy ground with partially disturbed or trampled herbaceous vegetation, with yellow Asteraceae, including roadside verges and Broadland river banks. Also recorded on chalk grassland. The species may have benefited from a reduction in verge trimming in recent years (TS).
- **FLOWERS VISITED** Asteraceae including beaked hawk's-beard, cat's-ear, mouse-ear-hawkweed, daisy. The first species was the main pollen source when bees first hatched at Weybourne. Cat's-ear flowered slightly later and the bees used it when it became available.
- **NESTING** A nesting aggregation at the top of Weybourne cliffs consisted of 250+ holes clustered in groups of up to 50 near the old pill box at the top of the cliffs during May 2015. Most of the nests were made on trampled paths on sandy/gravelly material with little vegetation.
- **PARASITES** *Nomada integra* (seemingly rare in Norfolk).

Andrena labialis Large Meadow Mining Bee

Females are large and broad. The clypeus and thorax hairs are pale, as are the hairs on the hind tibia. The abdomen is heavily punctate with narrow marginal bands on T3–T5. There are pale hairs on the abdomen tip. **Males** resemble small narrow females.

- **FLIGHT** May–July (BWARS).
- **DISTRIBUTION** Recorded in the county by Kirby 1802 and by Bridgman in the late 1800s: "not common Eaton, Harford Bridges, Brundall, Yarmouth, Lynn, June". No records since that time.
- **HABITAT** Grasslands with Fabaceae (BWARS).
- **FLOWERS VISITED** Uses Fabaceae (BWARS).
- **NESTING** Sometimes nests in aggregations (BWARS).
- **PARASITES** *Sphecodes rubicundus* (BWARS).

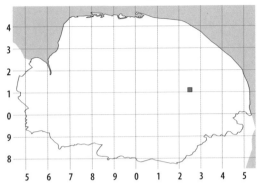

Andrena labiata Red-girdled Mining Bee

Females and males both have a red abdomen which is black at the base and the tip, making this bee very distinctive. The body hairs are pale. **Males** have a white area of cuticle on the clypeus with smaller patches of white adjacent. There are also white tufts of hair at each side of the clypeus.

- **FLIGHT** May–June.
- **DISTRIBUTION** Thinly distributed, mostly in the east of the county: possibly increasing.
- **HABITAT** Usually associated with germander speedwell, occurring in sheltered places on well established grasslands, including Weaver's Way and a garden near Blakeney.
- **FLOWERS VISITED** Germander speedwell, meadow saxifrage, wild strawberry, cistus.

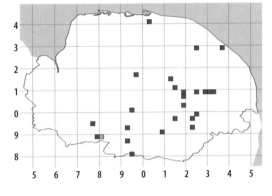

- **NESTING** Probably amongst grass in sandy places.
- **PARASITES** *Nomada guttulata* (BWARS).

♀ on buttercup, New Buckenham Common, 30 May

♂, New Buckenham Common, 30 May

Andrena lapponica Bilberry Mining Bee

Females are stocky bees with black hair on most parts of the body except the top of the thorax which has bright reddish brown hair and T1–T2 which have long pale brown hairs. The floccus is white. **Males** have pale hairs on the clypeus with dark hairs on the eye margins. The mandibles are long and curved with a triangular flange at the base. The thorax has reddish brown hair above and pale hair below and there are pale hairs on T1–T2. The cuticle is black.

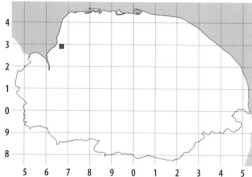

♀, Eyam Moor, Derbyshire, 7 May

- ■ **FLIGHT** May.
- ■ **DISTRIBUTION** There is one Norfolk record: a male from Dersingham Bog, 7 May 2016 (AM confirmed SF). The presence of a breeding population needs checking.
- ■ **HABITAT** Wet bog/heathland.
- ■ **FLOWERS VISITED** None observed in Norfolk. Considered specific to bilberry but none is present on Dersingham Bog. There is some cranberry and this is the likely food source. Females have been recorded on holly and other pollen sources outside Norfolk.
- ■ **NESTING** No Norfolk information.
- ■ **PARASITES** *Nomada panzeri* (BWARS).

♀ on bilberry, Eyam Moor, Derbyshire, 7 May

♂ on bilberry, Eyam Moor, Derbyshire, 7 May

Andrena marginata Small Scabious Mining Bee

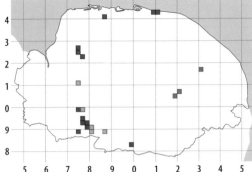

♀s on field scabious, Weybourne Camp, July (upper two) and on small scabious, Flitcham, August, showing colour variation

♂ on field scabious, Weybourne Camp, 31 July

Females have white hair on the clypeus and thorax. The hairs on the hind tibia are pale. The abdomen has variable amounts of orange cuticle and white marginal bands. The first tergite is always black. In the darkest forms the other tergites are also black but with an orange margin. The most orange form has clear orange tergites and intermediate forms have some black on the orange areas. The tibiae are often loaded with pink scabious pollen. **Males** have a white clypeus but are otherwise black. There are white hairs on the body including the margins of the tergites. The head has a ridge at the hind margins and the tongue is exceptionally long, probably an adaptation allowing it to reach nectar at the base of a scabious flower.

- ■ **FLIGHT** July–September, active later than *Andrena hattorfiana*.
- ■ **DISTRIBUTION** First recorded by Bridgman 1879 at Eaton and also by Wainright 1900 at West Runton and Atmore 1909 at Hunstanton. Most records are from chalky areas in the west of the county. There is a strong population on recreated chalk grassland (established 15 years) at Flitcham where it uses small scabious.
- ■ **HABITAT** Chalk grassland and coastal grassland with plenty of scabious.
- ■ **FLOWERS VISITED** Shows a strong preference for scabious, using both field scabious and small scabious. It occurs at some sites where there is field scabious but no small scabious.
- ■ **NESTING** No nests discovered in Norfolk so far.
- ■ **PARASITES** *Nomada argentata*.

Andrena minutula Common Mini-miner

Females are 7–8 mm long. The body hairs are pale yellow/white. The margins to the tergites have a row of white hairs, doubled to two rows at the edges. This is the commonest of the *Micrandrena* (Mini-miner) group in the county, but is difficult to separate from the other three likely Norfolk species without using microscopic features. **Males** are small and slender. The spring brood has black clypeus hairs but in the second brood they are pale. The body hairs are yellow/white and there are hairs on the abdomen similar to those of females but less distinct.

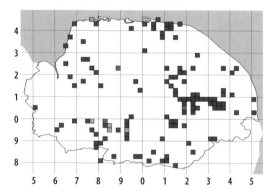

- ■ **FLIGHT** March–September in two broods.
- ■ **DISTRIBUTION** Widely distributed and common in the county.
- ■ **HABITAT** A wide range including gardens, field margins, scrub, woodland edge, verges and grasslands.

- ■ **FLOWERS VISITED** Bramble, dandelion, hogweed, garden goldenrod, ground-elder, white bryony. Pollen loads from Flitcham included bramble, daisy, hogweed, mayweed and wild carrot and from Weybourne *Potentilla* sp. (TW).
- ■ **NESTING** Nests in aggregations in broken sloping ground.
- ■ **PARASITES** *Nomada flavoguttata* (DB).

♀ on hogweed, Weybourne, June

♂ on goldenrod, Weybourne, 9 August

Andrena minutuloides Plain Mini-miner

It is necessary to use microscopic features to be confident of identifying this species. **Females** resemble *Andrena minutula* but have just one row of hairs on the tergite margins. The punctures on the thorax are less distinct. **Males** also resemble *A. minutula* but the hairs are whiter.

- ■ **FLIGHT** March–September.
- ■ **DISTRIBUTION** There are a few Norfolk records from the 19th century and a record from Stanta in the 1980s (BWARS). A female was recorded at Flitcham on 7 July 2013 (confirmed GE). Two possible males were found at the same site on 19 August 2013 and a further female on 21 June 2016 (all NO). This is a southern species and at the northern edge of its range in Norfolk
- ■ **HABITAT** Arable margin; chalk grassland.

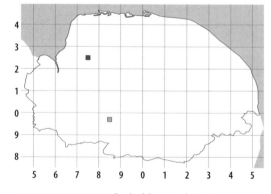

- ■ **FLOWERS VISITED** Probably mostly Apiaceae.
- ■ **NESTING** No information.
- ■ **PARASITES** *Nomada flavoguttata* (SF).

Andrena nigriceps Black-headed Mining Bee

Females have black hair on the clypeus, red-brown hair on the thorax and dark hairs on the tibia. The abdomen has broad marginal bands. **Males** have pale hairs on the face, reddish hairs on the thorax and long pale hairs on the tergites with fluffy marginal bands. The legs are black (SF).

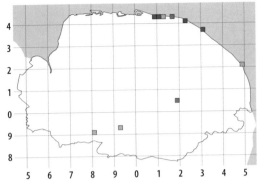

♀ at nest hole, Kelling Heath, 17 July

- **FLIGHT** July–August.
- **DISTRIBUTION** Described as "very abundant on Ragwort" at West Runton by Wainright 1901. Now a scarce species, recorded in the Brecks and on the coast between Weybourne and Winterton, including Beeston Common in the 1970s (KD). [Wainright 1901 also reports one specimen of *Andrena simillima* with *A. nigriceps* at West Runton; a species closely resembling *A. nigriceps* but with paler hair on the face and other body parts].
- **HABITAT** Heathland, cliff tops and scrub.
- **FLOWERS VISITED** Hogweed, black knapweed.
- **NESTING** A female was entering a nest hole in a sandy bank on Kelling Heath on 17 July 2016 (NO).
- **PARASITES** *Nomada rufipes* (BWARS).

♀ on hogweed, Weybourne, 13 July

Andrena nigroaenea Buffish Mining Bee

Females have a mixture of black and brown clypeal hairs, ginger brown hairs on the thorax and bright ginger hairs on the hind femur and tibia. The abdomen has a covering of short ginger hairs with prominent black hairs at the tip. **Males** closely resemble females in colour pattern.

- **FLIGHT** March–June.
- **DISTRIBUTION** Widespread and common in the county.
- **HABITAT** A wide range including gardens, hedgerows, heathland and scrub.
- **FLOWERS VISITED** Alexanders, blackthorn, bramble, garden heathers, gorse, green alkanet, oilseed rape, primrose, willows. A pollen load from North Creake contained Asteraceae sp., *Ranunculus* sp. and *Anthemis* sp. (TW).
- **NESTING** Nest aggregations found in a garden in Weybourne, an earth bank at Stanta and on a bank behind Weybourne beach. Males observed

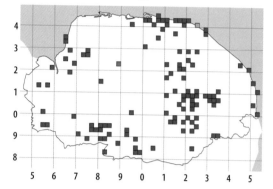

patrolling up and down hedgerows and along an earth bank containing nest burrows, flying 30–40 m in each direction.

- **PARASITES** A female with two *Stylops* sp. was recorded at Flitcham 2014. *Nomada fabriciana* (BWARS), *N. flava*, *N. goodeniana* (DB).

♀ at nest site, Weybourne beach, March

Part of a nest aggregation, Weybourne, April

♂, Southery, 11 April

There has been uncertainty about the distinction between these two large black species, but they have now been shown by DNA analysis to be genetically distinct. *Andrena pilipes* is thought to be more coastal than *A. nigrospina*. Flight times overlap (Jukes 2016).

Andrena nigrospina Scarce Black Mining Bee

♀ on cotoneaster, Browston, Great Yarmouth, July [AM]

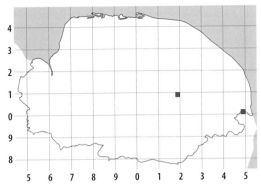

Females have a black cuticle and black hair with the exception of white tibial hairs. The wings are darkened. **Males** are also all black but with pale hairs on the thorax as well as the legs.

- ■ **FLIGHT** One brood May–early July, largely between the two flight periods of *Andrena pilipes*.
- ■ **DISTRIBUTION** "Occasionally taken around Norwich end of May and June" – as *A. pilipes*, (Bridgman 1879). Atmore 1909 describes it as "scarce" near King's Lynn. Two females were

recorded at Bowthorpe on 9 June 2011 (TS). A black female *Andrena* was photographed at Browston near Great Yarmouth in early July 2015 (AM): although coastal, the timing suggests *A. nigrospina* (TS).

- ■ **HABITAT** Brownfield site on sandy soil with a mix of wild and garden plants (scheduled for housing).
- ■ **FLOWERS VISITED** Brassicaceae, cotoneaster.
- ■ **NESTING** Not observed in Norfolk.
- ■ **PARASITES** A form of *Nomada fulvicornis* (SF).

Andrena pilipes Black Mining Bee

♀ (left) and ♂ (right) on cultivated *Eryngium*, Rainham Marshes, Essex, 6 August [TB]

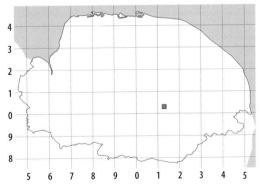

Double brooded: April–May and July–August. One *Andrena pilipes* (*s.l.*) recorded at Wymondham 20 April 1942. **Females** have slightly less extensive white hairs on the tibiae. **Males** can be separated by details of genitalia.

Andrena nitida Grey-patched Mining Bee

Females have pale clypeus hairs with black hairs round the bases of the antennae. There is rich red brown hair on the upper thorax grading to white beneath. The hind tibia has dark hairs above and white below. The tergites have an anterior band of long sparse white hairs, widening to hair tufts at the tergite edges. The tergites show a glossy shine through these hairs. **Males** have long white hairs on the clypeus and black hairs at the eye margins. The hair on the upper thorax is rich red. The tergites have sparse white hair bands widening at the sides, similar to those in females. The cuticle is black.

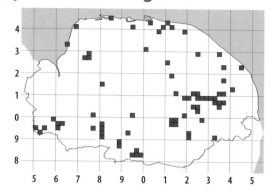

♀, Cambridge, 10 April

♂, Fowlmere, Cambridgeshire, 17 April

- **FLIGHT** April–June.
- **DISTRIBUTION** Widespread and common, though not seen in large numbers. It is fairly close to its northern British limit in north Norfolk. Although recorded by Bridgman in the 1800s there are no 20th century county records.
- **HABITAT** Gardens, hedgerows, orchards.

- **FLOWERS VISITED** Many kinds of spring blossom including apple, willows, blackthorn and hawthorn. Also visits alexanders, hedge parsley and yellow Brassicaceae. A pollen load from Kelling Heath was 100% blackthorn (TW).
- **NESTING** Not observed in Norfolk.
- **PARASITES** *Nomada goodeniana* (BWARS).

Andrena niveata Long-fringed Mini-miner

Recognised by long fringes of white hairs on the tergites. Two specimens collected near King's Lynn, Atmore 1909, are the only county records. The species is associated with Brassicaceae.

Andrena ovatula Small Gorse Mining Bee

Females have pale hairs on the clypeus. The thorax has grey-brown hairs and the hind tibia has pale hairs. The hind tibia and tarsus are translucent orange in about half of Norfolk specimens, the others having entirely black legs. This species is very similar to *Andrena wilkella*, one difference being that *A. ovatula* has a complete white hair band on T3 (narrowing/interrupted in *A. wilkella*). Worn specimens can be very difficult to separate. **Males** have a similar colour pattern to females, including a complete marginal band on T3 (interrupted in *A. wilkella* males). The legs are usually black but can be partially yellow/orange.

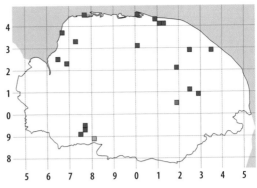

♀ on yellow melilot, Weybourne Camp, 2 August

♂ on yellow melilot, Weybourne Camp, 31 July

- **FLIGHT** April–September; two brooded.
- **DISTRIBUTION** Widely scattered records from the Brecks, western heaths, Cromer Ridge heaths, the Norwich area, East Ruston Common and coastal marshes.
- **HABITAT** Heaths and rough grassland with a gravelly substrate.
- **FLOWERS VISITED** Bramble, field bindweed, gorse, heather (ling), tormentil, yellow melilot.
- **NESTING** Female with a pollen load on a sandy path, Felmingham, 15 May 2015.
- **PARASITES** No *Nomada* species reported.

Andrena praecox Small Willow Mining Bee

Females have pale hairs on the clypeus with dark hairs along the eye margins. There are orange-brown hairs on the upper thorax grading into long pale hairs below the wings. The tibial hairs are pale above and dark below. The abdomen has long pale brown hairs on the first two tergites and shorter hairs thereafter. **Males** have long antennae and pale hairs on the clypeus. The mandibles are long and overlapping with a flange at the base. There are long sparse hairs on the first two tergites. The legs are black.

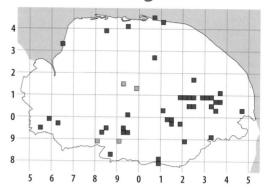

♀, Great Hockham, 8 April

- **FLIGHT** March–May.
- **DISTRIBUTION** Widespread records reflecting the presence of willows and sandy soils.
- **HABITAT** Sandy soils with willows.
- **FLOWERS VISITED** Pollen obtained from willows. Also seen visiting bird cherry and ground-elder.
- **NESTING** Nesting in earth loosened by moles amongst bracken near Thompson Common April 2015.
- **PARASITES** *Nomada ferruginata*.

♂ on alexanders, Walsey Hills, April

Andrena proxima Broad-faced Mining Bee

Norwich late 1800s: Saunders refers to a Norwich record by Bridgman (TS), but it is not included in Bridgman's published list. The species may still be present but overlooked. It occurs widely in Suffolk.

Andrena scotica Chocolate Mining Bee

Females have a mixture of brown and black hairs on the clypeus. The thorax has pale brown hair and there is a covering of fine brown hair on the abdomen. The hind tibia has black hairs above and white below (a feature shared with *Andrena nitida*). **Males** have pale brown hairs on the clypeus and thorax and a few sparse hairs on the rather shiny abdomen. Sometimes the margin of the second tergite is pale or reddish. The fourth antennal segment is long. The hind tarsus can be partially orange.

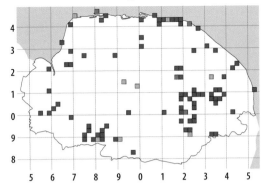

♀, Cambridge, 16 April

♀, Cambridge Botanic Garden, April

♂, Weybourne, 11 May

- ■ **FLIGHT** March–July.
- ■ **DISTRIBUTION** Widespread and common.
- ■ **HABITAT** Occurs in a wide range of habitats including gardens.
- ■ **FLOWERS VISITED** Apple, blackthorn, dandelion, hawthorn, hogweed, holly, bramble, poppy, sea holly. A pollen load from Flordon Common contained hawthorn and sycamore and a load from Swanton Novers sycamore and holly (TW).
- ■ **NESTING** No nests found.
- ■ **PARASITES** *Nomada marshamella* and *N. flava* (BWARS), and *Stylops* sp.

Andrena semilaevis Shiny-margined Mini-miner

Females can be distinguished from other *Micrandrena* species using microscopic features. The punctation on the clypeus and thorax is dense, similar to that in *Andrena minutula*, and there is fine punctation on T1 and T2, absent in *A. minutula* and *A. subopaca* (but present in *A. alfkenella*). The margins of tergites 2–4 are depressed and shiny in both sexes. **Males** have long white hairs on the clypeus, as long as the scape of the antennae and long white hairs on the thorax. There are white marginal bands on the abdomen, incomplete on T1 and T2. Punctation is similar to that of females.

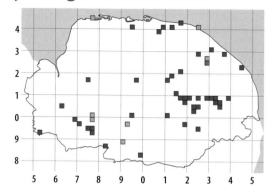

♀ on hedge parsley, Warham Camp, 19 June

- **FLIGHT** May–August.
- **DISTRIBUTION** Widespread and fairly common.
- **HABITAT** Verges, scrub, woodland edge, gardens, churchyards.

- **FLOWERS VISITED** Hedge parsley, germander speedwell.
- **NESTING** Not recorded.
- **PARASITES** *Nomada flavoguttata* (DB).

♂ on germander speedwell, Warham Camp, 25 May

Andrena subopaca Impunctate Mini-miner

Females have pale hairs on the clypeus. The punctures on the clypeus and thorax are more widely spaced than in other Mini-miners. The tergites have no clear punctures. There are white hair bands on the edges of the tergites. **Males** are similar to females in the above features.

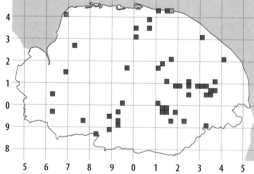

♀ on tormentil, Swanton Novers Great Wood, 13 May

- **FLIGHT** April–July.
- **DISTRIBUTION** Widespread and fairly common.
- **HABITAT** Possibly more associated with woodland than other mini-miner species in Norfolk.
- **FLOWERS VISITED** Bramble, cinquefoils, dandelion, germander speedwell, tormentil.
- **NESTING** Not observed.
- **PARASITES** *Nomada flavoguttata* (DB).

Andrena synadelpha Broad-margined Mining Bee

Females have pale hairs on the clypeus and dark hairs around the bases of the antennae. The abdomen bears reddish-brown hair. There are long brown hairs on the forward part of T2 and T3. The hind tibia has dark hairs above and pale below, the floccus hairs are white and the tip of the abdomen has black hairs. **Males** have pale hair on the clypeus, long antennae and long mandibles without a flange. There is reddish hair on the thorax and T1 and T2 have long pale hairs. The legs are black. Both sexes have wide margins to the tergites, though these are not easily seen in a photograph.

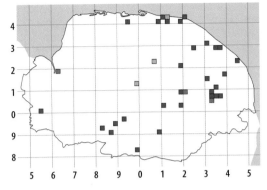

♀, Kelling Heath, 28 May

♀, Kelling Heath, 28 May

♂, Muckleborough Hill, 9 May

- ■ **FLIGHT** April–June.
- ■ **DISTRIBUTION** Widespread and can be moderately abundant but with fewer records from the west of the county.
- ■ **HABITAT** Woodland rides, heathland, churchyards, hedgerows.
- ■ **FLOWERS VISITED** Two females loaded with sycamore pollen on Kelling Heath, 26 May 2015. Also hogweed, hawthorn and hedge parsley.
- ■ **NESTING** Probably nesting in bracken debris below a sycamore tree on Kelling Heath. Males swarming in lee of hedgerow near Weybourne cliffs, May 2015.
- ■ **PARASITES** *Nomada panzeri* (DB).

Andrena tarsata Tormentil Mining Bee

Females have pale hairs on the clypeus and on top of the head. The thorax has short dark hairs above and longer pale hairs elsewhere. There are pale marginal bands on the abdomen. The hind tarsus and tibia are orange with pale yellow hairs.
Males have a white patch of cuticle on the clypeus which also bears white hairs. The thorax has dark hairs above and long white hairs on the sides. The abdomen has pale margins and the hind tarsi are orange.

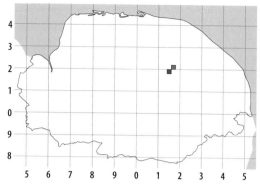

- ■ **FLIGHT** July–August.
- ■ **DISTRIBUTION** Bridgman refers to a male (as *Andrena analis*) collected at Felthorpe on June 29 1881. A female was recorded at Buxton Heath on 13 July 1979 (KD) and a male near Swannington (10 miles distant from Buxton Heath and close to Felthorpe) on 20 July 2010 (GN). These are the only county records.
- ■ **HABITAT** Acidic grassland with tormentil.
- ■ **FLOWERS VISITED** Oligolectic on tormentil.
- ■ **NESTING** Not observed.
- ■ **PARASITES** *Nomada roberjeotiana* (BWARS). Recorded near King's Lynn in 1902 by E A Atmore. *Andrena tarsata* is its only host.

♀ (above and below) on tormentil, New Forest, July

♂, Cornwall [PS]

Andrena thoracica Cliff Mining Bee

Females have black hairs on all body parts except for the upper thorax which has bright orange brown hairs. The tergites have few hairs and look shiny, with long black hairs at the tip of the abdomen. **Males** are similar in colour pattern to females, with long black clypeal hairs.

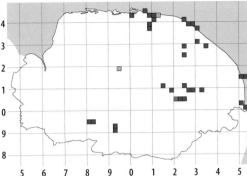

♀ second brood on bramble, Kelling Heath, July

- ■ **FLIGHT** March–August in two broods.
- ■ **DISTRIBUTION** Can be abundant in suitable habitats, including sandy grassland and brownfield sites around Norwich. Perhaps increasing. No records from the west of the county.
- ■ **HABITAT** Grassland, Brecks, heathland, soft cliffs.
- ■ **FLOWERS VISITED** Lesser celandine (first brood). Bramble, buddleia, hogweed, nipplewort and white bryony (second brood).
- ■ **NESTING** Aggregation of nest holes observed on a worn pathway on Kelling Heath, on the banks of the Cut-off Channel and on Weybourne cliffs.
- ■ **PARASITES** *Nomada fulvicornis* (TS) and *N. goodeniana* (BWARS).

♂, Kelling Heath, 7 April

♂s, Weybourne beach, 20 March

Andrena tibialis Grey-gastered Mining Bee

Females have pale hairs on the clypeus and white hair under the head. There is rich brown hair on the upper thorax and white hair beneath the wings. The propodeal pollen basket also has white hair. The hind tibia and tarsus are bright orange and the tibia hairs are pale, with a white floccus. The abdomen has a covering of pale hairs with black hairs at the tip. The pterostigma is orange-brown in both sexes. **Males** have a mix of black and brown clypeal hairs, the thorax has pale brown hairs and there are long brown hairs covering the tergites. The hind tarsus is orange and the hind tibia is orange distally.

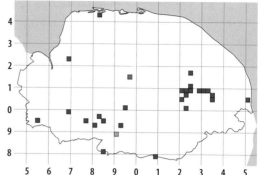

- ■ **FLIGHT** March–May.
- ■ **DISTRIBUTION** Frequent in the Norwich area and the Brecks.
- ■ **HABITAT** Sandy areas with willows.
- ■ **FLOWERS VISITED** Mainly uses willows. Also seen on *Pyracantha*.
- ■ **NESTING** Possible nest site in mole hill, near willows, Stanta. Males observed patrolling willows and bird cherry.
- ■ **PARASITES** *Nomada fulvicornis* (DB).

♀, Stanta, 28 April

Andrena tridentata Pale-tailed Mining Bee

Specimens are present in the Bridgman collection in Norwich Castle Museum. This species may now be extinct in the British Isles and perhaps in Europe (BWARS). The species was listed by Smith 1869 at Mousehold. Males were described as "not uncommon on Ragwort" in July near Norwich by Bridgman 1879 and "very abundant on Ragwort" at West Runton by Wainright 1901. There is a possible record from the Brecks TL77 in 1910 (Brecks Biodiversity Audit). The species was recorded in Suffolk up to 1944 (Norden Claypits: specimen of female in NHM).

Andrena trimmerana Trimmer's Mining Bee

Females of the first brood have dark hairs on the clypeus, pale brown hairs on the thorax, dark hairs on the upper side of the tibia and pale hairs below. The margins of T1–T2 are orange, though this colouring is variable. Second brood females have paler clypeal hairs (SF). **Males** show similar colouration to females. Spring males have a long spine at the base of each mandible. As in females the extent of red markings on the tergites is variable.

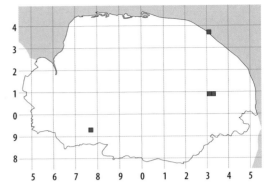

- **FLIGHT** All Norfolk records in July and August, but also has a spring brood (BWARS).
- **DISTRIBUTION** Described as "fairly common round Norwich" by Bridgman 1879, but owing to nomenclature changes it is not certain that he was referring to this species. There is a female specimen collected by KD in the Norwich Castle Museum, but this may have been collected outside Norfolk. Otherwise there are no further county records until two females were recorded at Brundall on 17–18 August 2013. A female was collected at Mundesley Cliffs and another at Cranwich Heath in early August 2015 and another female on 21 August 2015 at Brundall Countryside Park (all TS). These records are in widely spaced localities, suggesting a thinly spread but largely un-noticed population in the county. The national distribution is southern and these records may indicate a northern spread.
- **HABITAT** Heathland, coastal cliffs, parkland.
- **FLOWERS VISITED** Bramble, creeping thistle, fennel.
- **NESTING** Not observed.
- **PARASITES** *Nomada marshamella* (BWARS).

♀ on bramble, Cornwall [PS]

Andrena varians Blackthorn Mining Bee

Females have dark hairs on all body parts apart from bright ginger hairs on the thorax, white floccus hairs and long ginger brown hairs on T1 and T2, with shorter brown hairs on T3–T6.
Males show a similar colour pattern to females. The cuticle is black.

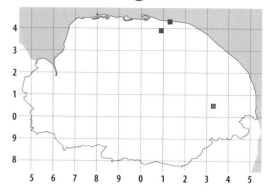

♀, Devil's Dyke, Cambridgeshire, 14 April

♀, Sheringham Park, 1 May

- **FLIGHT** All Norfolk records are from May, but it is known to emerge in April where blackthorn is abundant.
- **DISTRIBUTION** There are several specimens in Bridgman's 19th century collection, but there is only one possible record from the 20th century, which is a field observation from Wheatfen in 1936. In May 2011 a fresh female was photographed at Sheringham Park, and in May 2015 two females were recorded in parkland near Holt (both NO). This is a scarce species nationally.

- **HABITAT** Well established grassland adjacent to woodland or scrub.
- **FLOWERS VISITED** No observations: often associated with blackthorn (SF), but the recent Norfolk records coincided with the flowering of hawthorn.
- **NESTING** Not observed.
- **PARASITES** *Nomada panzeri* (DB).

Andrena wilkella Wilke's Mining Bee

This species closely resembles *Andrena ovatula*. **Females** have grey-brown hairs on the clypeus and thorax. The tibia hairs are also pale and there are white marginal bands on T1–T5. These bands narrow towards the centre, leaving a clear gap on T2 and T3 (entire on T3 in *A. ovatula*). The hind tibia and tarsus are orange. The tip of the abdomen is orange haired (darker in *A. ovatula*). **Males** show a similar colour pattern to females, also having interrupted abdominal bands on T2–T3.

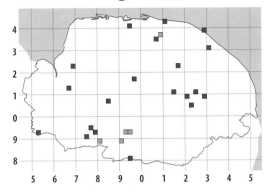

♀ on white clover, Hayling Island, Hampshire, July

♀, Hayling Island, Hampshire, July

- **FLIGHT** May–July, largely between the two broods of *Andrena ovatula*.
- **DISTRIBUTION** Recorded from widely scattered localities.
- **HABITAT** Sites include Cranwich Camp, Holt Lowes, Kelling Heath, Mousehold Heath and Santon Warren, but also occurs on calcareous grassland.

- **FLOWERS VISITED** Polylectic but often uses Fabaceae (SF).
- **NESTING** No information.
- **PARASITES** *Nomada striata* (DB); possibly *Sphecodes pellucidus* (BWARS).

Two members of this genus occur in the British Isles and both have been recorded in Norfolk, one for the first time in 2015. They are medium to small bees with long black hair and contrasting orange hairs on the legs. They have two sub-marginal cells and fairly short tongues and specialise in Asteraceae flowers. Nesting can occur in large aggregations usually on bare, fairly level ground.

Panurgus banksianus mating ball, Kelling Heath, 13 July

Panurgus banksianus ♀ at nest site with pollen load from cat's-ear, Kelling Heath, 20 July

Panurgus banksianus Large Shaggy Bee

Females have long black hairs on the clypeus and the head is broad. The thorax and abdomen have sparse black hairs and there is a fan of hairs encircling T5. The hind tibia and basitarsus bear long golden pollen hairs and there are shorter golden hairs on the mid tibiae. **Males** are similar but lack the very long hairs on the hind tibiae. The antennae are entirely black in both sexes.

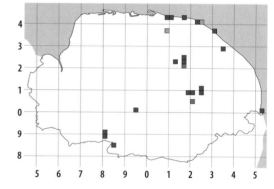

- **FLIGHT** June–August.
- **DISTRIBUTION** Most records are from the north-east coast, Marsham and Cawston Heaths, the Norwich area and the Brecks. Most are in the east of the county.
- **HABITAT** Acidic grasslands, cliffs and heaths with abundant yellow Asteraceae flowers.
- **FLOWERS VISITED** Cat's-ear, daisy, hawkbit, sulphur cinquefoil, yarrow. Torpid males may remain in cat's-ear flowers and become enclosed by them during the night (EAE).

- **NESTING** Nests in aggregations on flat ground, especially footpaths, e.g. Kelling Heath July 2015.
- **PARASITES** No bee cleptoparasites recorded in mainland Britain (BWARS).

♀ on cat's-ear, Kelling Heath, 28 July

♂, Kelling Heath, 13 July

Panurgus calcaratus Small Shaggy Bee

This is a much smaller species than *Panurgus banksianus*. Both sexes have partially orange antennae. **Males** have a small projection beneath the hind tibiae.

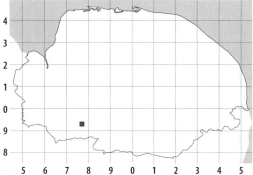

♀, Ibiza, April

- ■ **FLIGHT** August.
- ■ **DISTRIBUTION** There is only one definite county record, from Cranwich Heath in August 2015 (TS), which is the first record for the Brecks.
- ■ **HABITAT** Breckland grass heath.
- ■ **FLOWERS VISITED** No information.
- ■ **NESTING** No information.
- ■ **PARASITES** No bee cleptoparasites recorded in mainland Britain (BWARS).

♂ dormant in cool weather, Ibiza, April

Mating pair, Ibiza, April

The genera *Halictus* and *Lasioglossum* can be tricky to separate. All Halictidae have a groove, looking rather like a hair parting at the tip of the abdomen, called a rima. Most species have bands on the abdomen. In *Halictus* these are on the hind margins of the tergites, but in *Lasioglossum* they are at the front, often partly covered by the hind edge of the preceding tergite. In some species females have orange legs. Males have pale leg markings and a pale patch on the clypeus. Some species have a metallic greenish cuticle. The tongue is short and pollen is collected on the hind legs. Several members of the genus are eusocial, having larger egg-laying females (queens) and smaller sterile females (workers) which help at the nest. Nesting occurs in the ground, sometimes in aggregations. Only (mated) females survive the winter, with both sexes emerging from the first spring brood. The genus is parasitised by various *Sphecodes* bees. Six species have been recorded in mainland Britain with three in Norfolk.

Halictus rubicundus ♀ showing rima at tip of abdomen, Kelling Heath, 20 April

Lasioglossum leucozonium ♀ showing anterior tergite hair bands, Kelling Heath, 18 August

Halictus tumulorum ♀ showing posterior tergite bands, Holkham, 8 September

Halictus confusus Southern Bronze Furrow Bee

This species is very similar to *Halictus tumulorum*: please refer to that species for a description.

- **FLIGHT** Recorded in May, July and August.
- **DISTRIBUTION** Recorded at Roydon Common (MA) and in the Brecks, with fourt post-2000 records (GN, TS).
- **HABITAT** Sandy grassland, sometimes with heather (ling).
- **FLOWERS VISITED** No information.
- **NESTING** No information.
- **PARASITES** None known (BWARS).

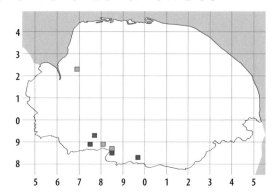

Halictus rubicundus Orange-legged Furrow Bee

Females: this bee could be mistaken for an *Andrena* but for the presence of a rima and the lack of facial foveae. The head and thorax hair is red and there are white marginal bands on the abdomen, interrupted centrally in T1 and T2. The cuticle and hair of the hind tibiae and the mid and hind tarsi is orange. **Males** are similar but slimmer with long antennae. The tibiae and tarsi of all legs are largely yellow but with a black mark on the tibiae and there is yellow mark on the clypeus. The labrum is also yellow.

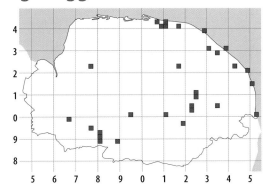

♀ at nest hole, Spalla Gap, Weybourne, 20 May

♂, Wharfedale, Yorkshire, 16 August

- **FLIGHT** April–August with males recorded from July.
- **DISTRIBUTION** Widespread in the Brecks and the east of the county.
- **HABITAT** Heathland and other habitats with gravelly soils, including Broadland (Hickling).
- **FLOWERS VISITED** Bramble, dandelion, oxeye daisy, Oxford ragwort, ploughman's-spikenard, ragwort, white bryony.
- **NESTING** Nesting aggregation on low cliff at Spalla Gap, Weybourne. A eusocial species (BWARS).
- **PARASITES** *Sphecodes gibbus* and *S. monilicornis* (BWARS).

Halictus tumulorum Bronze Furrow Bee

Females: this species is much smaller than the last and rather broad bodied. The cuticle has a dull greenish sheen, though this can be hard to see in some individuals. The tergites have dull white hind margins and also flattened hairs at the anterior tergite edges. Females of *Halictus confusus* are almost identical but have broader white margins to the tergites which do not narrow centrally (SF). **Males** are also metallic green. The antennae are very long and the tibia, tarsus and most of the femur of all legs are bright yellow. The mandibles, labrum and tip of the clypeus are also yellow. Males can be separated from *H. confusus* males only from details of genitalia.

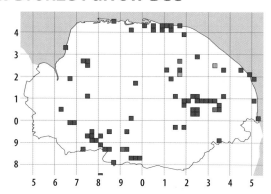

- **FLIGHT** April–October, with males recorded from June.
- **DISTRIBUTION** Widespread and common.
- **HABITAT** Woodland, heathland, churchyards, gardens, quarries, river valleys.
- **FLOWERS VISITED** Bramble, cinquefoils, dandelion, fleabane, germander speedwell, *Sedum*, mullein, ragwort, scabious, white bryony. Males are sometimes seen in clusters in one flower.
- **NESTING** Nests in aggregations. Eusocial: small females are likely to be sterile workers. No county information.
- **PARASITES** *Sphecodes ephippius* (SF).

♀, Cambridge Botanic Garden, 25 June

♂ on field scabious, Cambridge Botanic Garden, 12 September

This genus consists mostly of small dark bees which have a rima at the end of the abdomen. They differ from *Halictus* in (nearly all) having the hair bands on the tergites only at the base and not on the hind margin. The hair bands (consisting of hairs pressed down on the cuticle) become more exposed as the abdomen is stretched. Four Norfolk species have a metallic green/blue cuticle. The tongue is short. Pollen is collected on the hind legs and nesting is in the ground often in aggregations, with some species being eusocial. Mated females survive the winter, with males usually first appearing in early summer. Bees in the genus *Sphecodes* are often cleptoparasites, as is *Nomada sheppardana*. The wasp, *Cerceris rybyensis* often preys on *Lasioglossum* species. Thirty four species have been recorded in the British Isles, with 25 recorded in Norfolk, 23 post-2000. Many are difficult to identify without using microscopic features.

Lasioglossum sp. ♀ and *Megachile ligniseca* ♀ sharing a coneflower, Weybourne, 6 August

Lasioglossum calceatum ♂ on goldenrod, Beeston Common, 3 October. A pale spot on the clypeus is present in ♂'s of many *Lasioglossum* species

Lasioglossum pauxillum ♀ on coneflower, Weybourne, 13 August

Lasioglossum albipes Bloomed Furrow Bee

This species closely resembles the much commoner *Lasioglossum calceatum*. *L. albipes* is smaller with a longer face. Microscopic examination is needed to confirm identity.

- **FLIGHT** May–September with males recorded only in August–September.
- **DISTRIBUTION** Widely distributed, not common.
- **HABITAT** Brecks, cliffs, commons, parkland, woodland rides.
- **FLOWERS VISITED** Yellow Asteraceae, bramble.
- **NESTING** No Norfolk records.
- **PARASITES** *Sphecodes monilicornis* (SF).

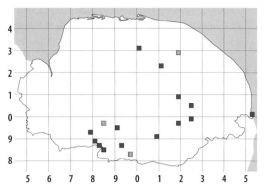

♀ on lesser celandine, Derbyshire, 4 May

Lasioglossum brevicorne Short-horned Furrow Bee

Microscopic examination is needed to confirm identity. **Females** have a shiny thorax and pale wing stigmas. There are hair patches on T2 and T3 and the end of the abdomen has many white hairs. **Males** have short antennae. The mandibles and lower clypeus are yellow but the labrum is black (SF).

- **FLIGHT** Females recorded May–September.
- **DISTRIBUTION** Recorded from Roydon Common 1996 (MA), Thetford Warren 1983 (Brecks Project), Santon Warren 2011, 2014, 2015 (TS) and Winterton Dunes 2014 (TS). A scarce species nationally.
- **HABITAT** Sandy heathland.
- **FLOWERS VISITED** No information.
- **NESTING** No information.
- **PARASITES** Possibly *Sphecodes puncticeps* (BWARS).

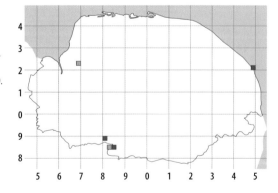

Lasioglossum calceatum Common Furrow Bee

Females: the face is round with dense punctation. The body hair is pale rusty brown and there are white hair patches on the tergites. These show through the transparent margin of the preceding tergite, making the edges look orange. **Males** are long and slim with dark antennae and a pale mark on the clypeus. The tarsi and each end of the tibiae are pale. Some have red areas of cuticle on the abdomen.

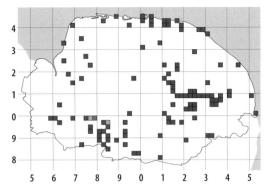

- **FLIGHT** April–September. Males from June.
- **DISTRIBUTION** Widespread: probably the commonest member of the genus in the county.
- **HABITAT** Commons, heathland, parkland, gardens, river valleys, green lanes, coastal sites but not dunes.
- **FLOWERS VISITED** Angelica, aster, yellow Asteraceae, cherry plum, cinquefoils, fennel, greater spearwort, hemp-agrimony, hogweed, ivy, marsh helleborine, great mullein, marjoram, rowan, garden sea holly, small scabious, field scabious, spear thistle, speedwells, thyme, tormentil.
- **NESTING** Nest aggregations observed on track Weybourne Camp, path at Wymondham and in a garden lawn, where each hole had 3–4 cm turrets (TS).
- **PARASITES** *Sphecodes monilicornis* and possibly *S. ephippius* (SF).

♀, Thriplow, Cambridgeshire, 24 March

♂, dark form, on goldenrod, Beeston Common, 3 October

♂, red form, on goldenrod, Beeston Common, 3 October

Lasioglossum cupromicans Turquoise Furrow Bee

One of four species with a metallic cuticle. **Females** have a long face, shiny punctured thorax and poorly defined white anterior hair bands on the abdomen. **Males** are similar with pale yellow undersides to the antennae.

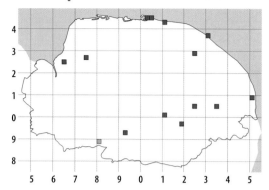

♀, Sheringham Park, 29 August

- **FLIGHT** May–September. Males from July.
- **DISTRIBUTION** Widely scattered across the county but not common.
- **HABITAT** Hot sandy places such as Blakeney Point, Weybourne Camp, Caistor Quarry and Santon Warren, but also Flordon Common and Wymondham Cemetery.
- **FLOWERS VISITED** No information.
- **NESTING** No records.
- **PARASITES** Possibly *Sphecodes geoffrellus* (SF).

Lasioglossum fratellum Smooth-faced Furrow Bee

This species requires microscopic examination for identification. **Females** have an oval face, a dull thorax and shiny first tergite, but no obvious hair patches on the tergite margins. The wing stigmas are pale brown. **Males** have very long antennae which are orange beneath, a feature shared with *Lasioglossum fulvicorne*. The labrum is orange and the tip of the clypeus is pale yellow. The tarsi are also orange-yellow.

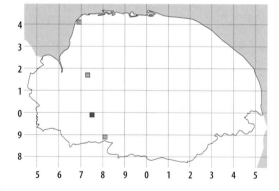

- **FLIGHT** Recorded in July.
- **DISTRIBUTION** Four records, all from the west of the county.
- **HABITAT** Sites include chalk grassland (Ringstead Downs) and base poor sites (Santon Warren, East Walton Common).
- **FLOWERS VISITED** No information.
- **NESTING** No records. A eusocial species (BWARS).
- **PARASITES** *Sphecodes hyalinatus* is a cleptoparasite (BWARS).

Lasioglossum fulvicorne Chalk Furrow Bee

Females have a round face and a dull thorax. The wing stigmas are pale. T1 lacks punctures and looks shiny. There are small hair patches on the anterior edges of the tergites. **Males** have very long antennae which are orange beneath, as in *Lasioglossum fratellum*. There is a yellow spot at the base of the clypeus, but the labrum and mandibles are black. The tarsi and parts of the tibiae are yellow.

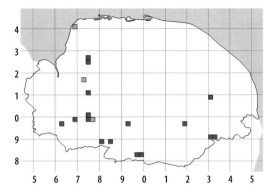

♀, Cambridge Botanic Garden, 25 June

- **FLIGHT** April–August. Males from July.
- **DISTRIBUTION** Most records are from the west of the county, but also found farther east, for example at Ditchingham.
- **HABITAT** Recorded from calcareous sites such as Ringstead Downs, Middle Harling Heath and Flitcham, but also on short grasslands which appear more acidic such as East Walton Common. At Ditchingham it is present on a rabbit nibbled grassy bank.
- **FLOWERS VISITED** Wild mignonette.
- **NESTING** No records. A solitary species (BWARS).
- **PARASITES** *Sphecodes hyalinatus* is a cleptoparasite (BWARS).

Lasioglossum lativentre Furry-claspered Furrow Bee

This species requires microscopic examination for identification. **Females** have a shiny punctured thorax and anterior hair bands on T2–T4 and are very similar to *Lasioglossum quadrinotatum*. The latter has a pale wing stigma but it is brown in *L. lativentre*. **Males** have similar punctation and hair patches. The labrum and tip of the clypeus are pale yellow as are the tarsi and each end of the tibiae; a pattern seen in the males of several species.

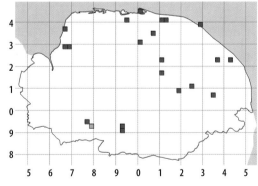

♂ paralysed by *Cerceris rybyensis* wasp, Kelling Heath, 16 August

- **FLIGHT** April–September. Males from August.
- **DISTRIBUTION** Widespread but not common.
- **HABITAT** Broads, river valleys, coastal marshes, brownfield sites, woodland rides, heathland.
- **FLOWERS VISITED** Dandelion, heather (ling), ragwort, perennial sowthistle, smooth hawk's-beard.
- **NESTING** No Norfolk information.
- **PARASITES** *Sphecodes ephippius* and *S. puncticeps* are cleptoparasites (SF).

Lasioglossum leucopus White-footed Furrow Bee

One of four species with a metallic sheen. **Females** have a round face and a dull punctate thorax. The tergites have shiny margins and lack clear hair bands. The body and leg hairs are white. The very similar *Lasioglossum morio* is slimmer with a longer face and the tergite margins have microscopic sculpturing. **Males**: the undersides of the antennae are buff. The labrum and lower clypeus and the tarsi and each end of the tibiae are yellow. The tergite margins are shiny as in females.

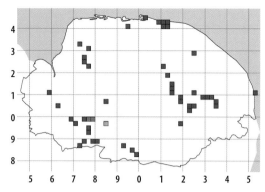

♀, Weybourne Beach, 27 March

♂, Massingham, 30 July

- **FLIGHT** March–October. Males from June.
- **DISTRIBUTION** Widespread and common.
- **HABITAT** Places with light soils including coastal sites, quarries, heathland and chalk grassland.
- **FLOWERS VISITED** Perennial sowthistle and other yellow Asteraceae.
- **NESTING** Present at a nest site on 3 October 2012 on a sloping sandy cliff on Kelling Heath.
- **PARASITES** Possibly *Sphecodes geoffrellus* (BWARS).

Lasioglossum leucozonium White-zoned Furrow Bee

Females: one of the larger more robust species with a round face and bold hair bands on the anterior edges of the tergites. The thorax punctures are surrounded by micro-reticulation making it look dull. **Males** are similar. The tip of the clypeus is pale but the labrum is black. There are white marks at the top of each tibia. The basitarsi are white at the upper end with a dark tip and the rest of the tarsi are dark.

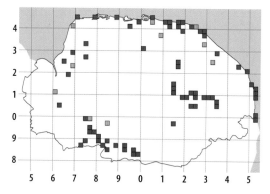

♀, Kelling Heath, 18 August

♂ on fleabane, Beeston Common, 27 August

- **FLIGHT** May–September. Males from late June.
- **DISTRIBUTION** One of the commoner *Lasioglossum* species in the county with most records coming from the Brecks, the Cromer Ridge, the coast and the Norwich area.
- **HABITAT** Lighter soils of gardens, quarries, heathland, soft cliffs, saltmarsh, chalk grassland, dunes.
- **FLOWERS VISITED** Mostly Asteraceae including cat's-ear, perennial sowthistle, fleabane, knapweed, nipplewort, ragwort, Oxford ragwort and creeping thistle (male). Also meadow saxifrage.
- **NESTING** On hard packed gravel on pill box, Weybourne cliff edge. Sometimes nests in aggregations (BWARS).
- **PARASITES** *Sphecodes ephippius* (BWARS).

Lasioglossum malachurum Sharp-collared Furrow Bee

Females: the head is broad and the thorax is dull and punctured. The pronotum forms prominent angles at the corners, just behind each eye. There are hair patches in the corners of T2 and T3 and the tergite margins look brownish where the hair bands show through. The body and leg hairs are pale brown. **Males** have ochre coloured undersides to the antennae and have protonal angles similar to those of females. The mandibles, labrum and tip of the clypeus are yellow. The tarsi are white except for the final segment. The tibiae are also white with a dark marking.

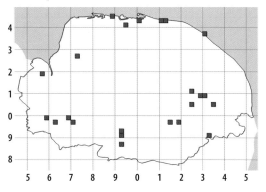

♀ at nest hole, Weybourne cliff, 22 May

♀, Weybourne, March

♂, Warham Camp, 3 September

♂, Sheringham Park, August

- ■ **FLIGHT** March–August. Males from July.
- ■ **DISTRIBUTION** Widely distributed in the county. This species has expanded its range northwards since the 1990s though it was recorded in the county in the 19th century. North Norfolk is at the northern edge of its current British range.

- ■ **HABITAT** Quarries, commons, chalk grassland, heathland, woodland rides.
- ■ **FLOWERS VISITED** Daisy, viper's-bugloss, garden geranium, field bindweed.
- ■ **NESTING** Nests in aggregations on bare ground such as paths. This is a eusocial species (BWARS).
- ■ **PARASITES** *Sphecodes monilicornis* (BWARS).

Lasioglossum minutissimum Least Furrow Bee

This is a very small species as its name suggests. **Females** look black and shiny with dark wing stigmas and white body hairs. There are very small hair patches on the anterior corners of T2 and T3. **Males** are similar and the cuticle is entirely black except for a barely visible small pale mark on the clypeus.

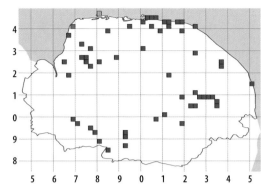

♀ on garden coneflower, Weybourne, 13 July

♂ on ragwort, Massingham, 30 July

- ■ **FLIGHT** March–September. Males from June.
- ■ **DISTRIBUTION** Common and widespread.
- ■ **HABITAT** Gardens, commons, heathland, woodland (sometimes under canopy), coastal sites.

- ■ **FLOWERS VISITED** Cat's-ear, coneflower, corn marigold, lesser celandine, ragwort, wild parsnip, ramsons.
- ■ **NESTING** Nesting aggregations observed on sloping or vertical banks on heathland and coastal paths.
- ■ **PARASITES** *Sphecodes longulus* (SF).

Lasioglossum morio Green Furrow Bee

This is one of the four species with a metallic sheen. **Females** have a slim build and a long face. The thorax is a dull green and there are hair bands on the anterior of T2–T4. **Males** are slender with very long antennae with ochre coloured undersides and a yellow mark on the clypeus. The legs are dark.

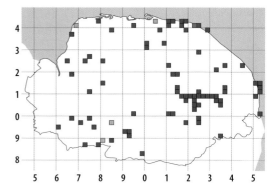

- **FLIGHT** March–October. Males from June.
- **DISTRIBUTION** Widespread and common.
- **HABITAT** Gardens, parkland, quarries, commons, cliffs, heathland, chalk grassland, river valleys, woodland rides.
- **FLOWERS VISITED** Yellow Asteraceae, cinquefoil, cornflower, creeping thistle, dandelion, fennel, germander speedwell, ground-ivy, hogweed, lavender, ragwort, ramsons, garden sea holly, sowthistles.

- **NESTING** Nesting aggregations at Kelling Heath, Stoke Ferry and in a cliff at Overstrand. Nests in broken earth banks. A eusocial species (BWARS).
- **PARASITES** *Sphecodes niger* and possibly other *Sphecodes* species. (BWARS).

♀, Thriplow, Cambridgeshire, 19 June

♂ on willowherb sp., Thriplow, Cambridgeshire, September

Lasioglossum nitidiusculum Tufted Furrow Bee

This species requires microscopic features for identification. **Females** have a round face and no hair bands on the tergites. **Males** have long antennae and partially yellow legs (SF).

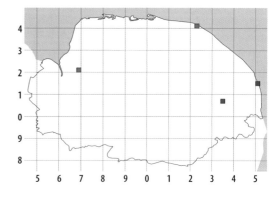

- **FLIGHT** March–August.
- **DISTRIBUTION** There is a male specimen from Cromer August 1971 in the Norwich Castle Museum (KD confirmed TS), annotated 'nest hole in cliff face'. A female was recorded in March and another in May at Strumpshaw Fen 2006 (TS). Another female was recorded at California Cliffs in July 2015 (TS). The species has declined nationally (BWARS).
- **HABITAT** Coastal cliffs, river valleys.
- **FLOWERS VISITED** No records.
- **NESTING** Cliff faces.

- **PARASITES** Small *Sphecodes* species and *Nomada sheppardana* (BWARS).

Lasioglossum parvulum Smooth-gastered Furrow Bee

Females have a round face and dull thorax. The wing stigma is mid-brown and there are no clear hair bands on the abdomen. T1 has few punctures and looks shiny. **Males** have long antennae which are yellow ochre beneath. The mandibles and the tip of the clypeus are yellow. The labrum can be dark or yellow. The basitarsi are dark but the rest of the tarsi can be partially orange-yellow and each end of the tibia is often orange-brown.

- **FLIGHT** March–October. Males from July.
- **DISTRIBUTION** Common with fewer records in the west of the county.
- **HABITAT** Gardens, quarries, commons, heathland, woodland rides, river valleys, Brecks.
- **FLOWERS VISITED** Alexanders, perennial sowthistle, dandelion, gipsywort, goldenrod, gorse, ground-elder, hawkbits, hogweed, purple-loosestrife, oxeye daisy, red dead-nettle, smooth hawk's-beard, snowdrop, white dead-nettle.
- **NESTING** Nest aggregations in sand pits at Stanta, Strumpshaw Fen and Kelling Heath and cleared ground at Sheringham Park; also in root plates at Stanta, Sheringham Park and Hoe Rough. Males patrolling gorse at Holt Lowes.
- **PARASITES** Several small *Sphecodes* species and *Nomada sheppardana* (BWARS).

♀ on hogweed, Weybourne, 21 June

♂ on goldenrod, Felbrigg, 14 August

Lasioglossum pauperatum Squat Furrow Bee

Females: a small squat species with a wide head and no clear hair bands on the tergites. The thorax is shiny with fairly sparse punctures. **Males** have yellow mandibles, labrum and lower clypeus. The tarsi are also pale.

- **FLIGHT** May–August. Males from August.
- **DISTRIBUTION** Recorded on the Cromer Ridge and Caistor Quarry. A scarce species nationally, confined to the south and east and reported as declining.
- **HABITAT** Quarry and sandy coastal grassland.
- **FLOWERS VISITED** No records.
- **NESTING** Up to 15 females recorded at Caistor Quarry so presumably breeding there (TS).
- **PARASITES** None known (SF).

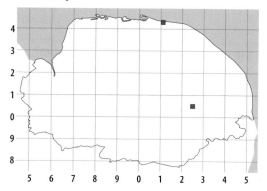

Lasioglossum pauxillum Large-spurred Furrow Bee

Females have a round face and the tips of the antennae are partially yellow beneath. The thorax is dull and punctate and there are no obvious hair bands on the abdomen. The wing stigmas are pale yellow-brown with a darker hind margin. The hind tibial spur is lobed: a microscopic feature which is diagnostic. **Males**: the undersides of the antennae are yellow and there is a yellow mark on the clypeus and sometimes the labrum and mandibles are also yellow. The tarsi are yellow and the tibiae can be partially so.

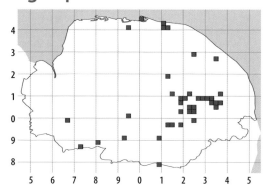

- **FLIGHT** April–September. Males from June.
- **DISTRIBUTION** Fairly common in the county, especially in the Norwich area. A southerly species nationally which is increasing.
- **HABITAT** Commons, quarries, gardens, river valleys, parks, heathland.
- **FLOWERS VISITED** Wild carrot, yellow Asteraceae, hogweed, wild mignonette, yarrow.
- **NESTING** A eusocial species which nests in aggregations (BWARS). Nest entrances can have small turrets of mud. A nesting aggregation near Methwold was mixed with nests of *Lasioglossum malachurum* and other *Lasioglossum* species.
- **PARASITES** Possibly *Sphecodes crassus* (BWARS).

♀ at nest site (above and below), Methwold, 6 July

♂ on wild mignonette, Warham Camp, 3 September

Lasioglossum prasinum Grey-tailed Furrow Bee

Females have very broad hair bands on the tergite margins with further white hair on the front edges of T1 and on the surface of T3–T5, making the hind parts of the abdomen look whitish. **Males** have red cuticle on T7, which is downcurved (SF).

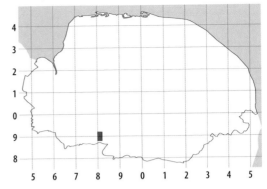

♀, New Forest, July

♀, New Forest, July

- **FLIGHT** May–August.
- **DISTRIBUTION** Recorded at Santon Warren 1986 (Brecks Project), Weeting 2011 and Grimes Graves 2009, 2011 (GN).
- **HABITAT** Forest rides and glades in the Brecks.
- **FLOWERS VISITED** No information.
- **NESTING** No nests recorded. Nests in aggregations.
- **PARASITES** Possibly *Sphecodes reticulatus* and *S. pellucidus* (BWARS).

Lasioglossum punctatissimum Long-faced Furrow Bee

Females have a long face with a raised clypeus and supraclypeus and short antennae. Most of the body surface is covered in dense punctures. There are hair bands on the front corners of T2 and T3. The wing stigmas are dark. **Males** have short antennae with rather bulging segments, partially orange beneath. The basitarsi are yellow with the lower tarsi being yellow suffused with black.

- **FLIGHT** March–August. Males from July.
- **DISTRIBUTION** Widely distributed but with no records for central Norfolk or the east coast.
- **HABITAT** Largely recorded on heathland and forest rides but also on Blakeney Point and Scolt Head Island.
- **FLOWERS VISITED** Bramble, cat's-ear, gorse, sea-lavender, scurvygrass, stork's-bill.

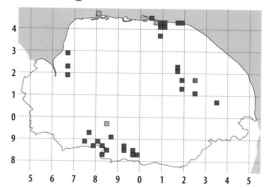

- **NESTING** Nest holes at a sandy cliff and on artificial gravel bee bank, Kelling Heath.
- **PARASITES** No British information.

♀, Kelling Heath, 27 April

♂, Beeston Common, 2 August

Lasioglossum puncticolle Ridge-cheeked Furrow Bee

This species requires microscopic examination for identification. **Females** are similar to *Lasioglossum villosulum* in having a shiny thorax with widely spaced deep punctures, but *L. puncticolle* has ridges under the sides of the head beneath the eyes. **Males** have mandibles, labrum and base of the clypeus yellow and also have pale tarsi and parts of the tibiae (SF).

- **FLIGHT** July.
- **DISTRIBUTION** There is only one county record, a female from East Winch Common July 2012 (TS). The species is largely confined to the south-east of England.
- **HABITAT** Acidic grassland with heather and gorse.
- **FLOWERS VISITED** No records.

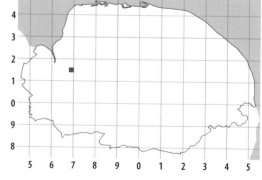

- **NESTING** No records.
- **PARASITES** None known (BWARS).

Lasioglossum quadrinotatum Four-spotted Furrow Bee

♂ on mayweed, Massingham, 30 July

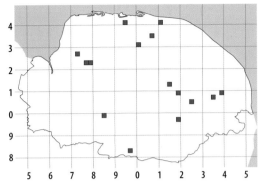

Females: there are prominent hair bands on the anterior part of T2 and T3. The wing stigmas are pale orange (darker in the similar *Lasioglossum lativentre*) and there are differences in the punctation of T1, visible with magnification. **Males**: the antennae are black. The tip of the clypeus and labrum are yellow as are the tarsi and both ends of the tibiae. These features are very similar to those of *L. lativentre*, but they can be distinguished from differences in their genitalia.

- **FLIGHT** April–July.
- **DISTRIBUTION** Widely scattered but not common. This is a scarce species nationally.
- **HABITAT** Chalk grassland, green lanes, woodland rides, churchyards, quarries, commons, river valleys.
- **FLOWERS VISITED** Dandelion, hogweed, mayweed, white bryony.
- **NESTING** No records.
- **PARASITES** Possibly *Sphecodes ephippius* and *S. puncticeps* (SF).

Lasioglossum sexnotatum Ashy Furrow Bee

Females: a large species with a dull punctured thorax and a shiny abdomen with striking white hair patches on T2–T4. **Males** are similar with long antennae which are yellow beneath (SF).

- **FLIGHT** Recorded in April and August.
- **DISTRIBUTION** Three Norfolk records: TL88 in April 1913, at Buckenham Tofts August 1985 (AF) and a female at Mundford Churchyard 16 July 2016 (AI). This is a rare species nationally but there are some recent records from Suffolk.
- **HABITAT** Buckenham Tofts is in the Stanford Training Area. The habitat is grassland, woodland and scrub with sheep grazing. Mundford churchyard is irregularly mown grass.
- **FLOWERS VISITED** Observed on thistles at Elveden and white bryony at Mundford.
- **NESTING** No information.
- **PARASITES** None known (SF).

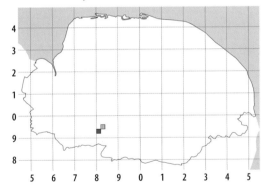

♀, Ipswich, May [NS]

Lasioglossum smeathmanellum Smeathman's Furrow Bee

♀, Felbrigg, 14 August

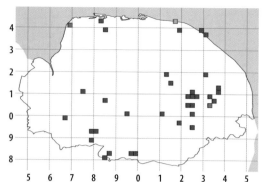

One of four species with a metallic sheen: very similar to *Lasioglossum cupromicans* and requiring microscopic features to separate. **Females** have an oval head (narrower in *L. cupromicans*), a shiny punctured thorax and metallic green tergites (blacker in *L. cupromicans*) with hair bands on T2–T4 (less marked in *L. cupromicans*). **Males** have a yellow spot on the clypeus (usually absent in *L. cupromicans*).

- **FLIGHT** April–September. Males from July.
- **DISTRIBUTION** Widely distributed but few recorded in the coastal zone despite comments by BWARS that it often nests in soft cliffs.
- **HABITAT** Quarries, gardens, churchyards, chalk grassland, forest rides.
- **FLOWERS VISITED** Daisy, garden bellflower, flixweed, oxeye daisy, yarrow.
- **NESTING** Nests observed in a brick wall and in the mortar of several stone churches (TS). Not eusocial (BWARS).
- **PARASITES** None known (BWARS)

Lasioglossum villosulum Shaggy Furrow Bee

♂ on cat's-ear, Kelling Heath, 28 July

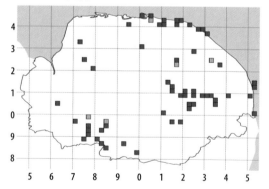

Females: the face is round and the thorax has widely spaced punctures. The body hair is white but there are no hair bands on the abdomen. **Males**: the antennae are short and yellow beneath and the face is long. There are no yellow marks on the clypeus but the tarsi are pale yellow. The pterostigma is pale with a darker hind margin.

- **FLIGHT** April–September. Males from July.
- **DISTRIBUTION** Widespread and common but with few records for central areas.

- **HABITAT** Brownfield sites, commons, quarries, cliffs, heathland, woodland rides, chalk grassland, Brecks.
- **FLOWERS VISITED** Yellow Asteraceae including cat's-ear, perennial sowthistle, dandelion, hawkbits, smooth hawk's-beard, oxeye daisy.
- **NESTING** Observed at a sandpit at Strumpshaw (TS). Not eusocial (BWARS).
- **PARASITES** Possibly *Sphecodes puncticeps* (SF). The distribution of *S. puncticeps* in Norfolk is consistent with this.

Lasioglossum xanthopus Orange-footed Furrow Bee

This is the largest British *Lasioglossum*. **Females**: the thorax has red hair and there are broad hair bands on T2–T4. The hind tibiae and tarsi are orange. They resemble *Halictus rubicundus* but in *L. xanthopus* the hair bands are at the anterior edge of the tergites rather than the hind margin. **Males** are large with brown hair on the thorax (SF).

- **FLIGHT** April–August. Males from August (BWARS).
- **DISTRIBUTION** There is one county record, from Caister 1902. This species has been found recently in the Suffolk Brecks and the Newmarket area. Its specific parasite, *Sphecodes spinulosus*, was recorded at Flitcham in 2013. It is a scarce species nationally.
- **HABITAT** Chalk grassland and soft cliffs.
- **FLOWERS VISITED** A wide variety (BWARS).
- **NESTING** Forms nesting aggregations (BWARS).
- **PARASITES** *Sphecodes spinulosus* (BWARS).

♀ on greater knapweed, Heydon, Cambridgeshire, 14 June

♀ on greater knapweed, Heydon, Cambridgeshire, 14 June

Lasioglossum zonulum Bull-headed Furrow Bee

Females are very similar to *Lasioglossum leucozonium* but have sparser punctation on T1 (requires microscope) and a paler wing stigma. **Males** have black legs (*L. leucozonium* has white basitarsi).

- **FLIGHT** April–October. Males from June (BWARS).
- **DISTRIBUTION** There is one record, from West Runton 1900 by Wainright.
- **HABITAT** Woodland rides and coast avoiding calcareous soils (BWARS).
- **FLOWERS VISITED** A wide range of species (BWARS).
- **NESTING** A solitary species (BWARS).
- **PARASITES** *Sphecodes scabricollis* (BWARS).

Bees in this genus are cleptoparasites which lay their eggs in the nests of *Halictus*, *Lasioglossum* and *Andrena* species. They have little hair and are mostly black with a partially red abdomen, a rough cuticle and strong mandibles. In most species mated females hibernate through the winter and appear in the spring, with males emerging later in the season. In all species females have a red abdomen with a dark tip. Males usually have red or yellowish bands on the abdomen but in one or two species the abdomen can be entirely black and can be confused with a *Lasioglossum*. The antennae of males are knobbly with a flattened hair patch on each segment. A few *Sphecodes* are specific to their host but others have several hosts and there is still much to learn about host choice. Seventeen species have been recorded from the British Isles with 15 recorded in Norfolk, 13 post-2000. It is usually difficult to identify members of this genus from images alone. Male identification sometimes relies on details of genitalia.

Sphecodes pellucidus ♀ exploring the nest entrance of *Andrena barbilabris*, Kelling Heath, 18 May

Sphecodes niger ♀ on germander speedwell, Coploe Hill, Cambridgeshire, 27 April

Sphecodes crassus Swollen-thighed Blood Bee

Females: recogniseable with magnification by their swollen hind femora and long labrum.
Males require examination of details of antennae and genitalia for identificaton.

Sphecodes ?crassus at *Lasioglossum pauxillum* nest, Methwold, 6 July

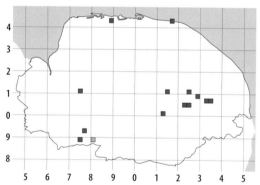

- **FLIGHT** March–August. Males from June.
- **DISTRIBUTION** Recorded in the Norwich area and the Brecks with outlying records from Holkham, Beeston Common, Narborough and Wymondham.
- **HABITAT** Quarry, old railway track, heathland, river valley.
- **FLOWERS VISITED** Angelica, cow parsley, wild carrot.
- **NESTING** Recorded near *Lasioglossum parvulum* nests at Mousehold Heath (TS). Other possible hosts include *L. puncatissimum* and *L. pauxillum* (SF).

Sphecodes ephippius Bare-saddled Blood Bee

This one of the larger species. **Females**: the punctation on the thorax is moderately dense. The red on the abdomen commonly extends to the sides of T4 and the spines on the legs are translucent reddish in colour. **Males** have short lumpy antennae, dense punctation on the thorax and red markings on T1–T3. The tibiae are black but the tarsi are pale.

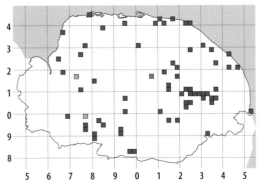

♀, Muckleburgh, 12 July

- ■ **FLIGHT** March–September. Males from June.
- ■ **DISTRIBUTION** Widespread and common.
- ■ **HABITAT** Heathland, quarries, commons, Brecks, woodland rides, chalk grassland, gardens.
- ■ **FLOWERS VISITED** Cat's-ear, hogweed, milk parsley, creeping thistle, turnip.
- ■ **NESTING** A parasite of *Halictus tumulorum* whose Norfolk distribution it closely matches. It is also thought to parasitise several *Lasioglossum* species (SF).

♂, Beeston Common, 1 August

Sphecodes ferruginatus Dull-headed Blood Bee

Females have dense puncturing on the face and thorax and a long labrum. **Males**: tergites 1–3 are often entirely red but males require microscopic examination to confirm (SF).

- ■ **FLIGHT** No Norfolk information.
- ■ **DISTRIBUTION** Only one Norfolk record by Bridgman from Brundall in the 1880s.
- ■ **HABITAT** No information.
- ■ **FLOWERS VISITED** No records.
- ■ **NESTING** *Lasioglossum fulvicorne*, *L. fratellum* and *L. pauxillum* are possible hosts (SF).

Sphecodes geoffrellus Geoffroy's Blood Bee

Females: the mandibles of this small species have two points and the punctures on the thorax are shallow and well spaced. The tarsi and bases of the tibiae are orange. There is often a black spot at the side of the abdomen where T2 meets T3. **Males** have variable yellow/red bands on T1–T4. The tarsi are reddish as are both ends of the tibiae.

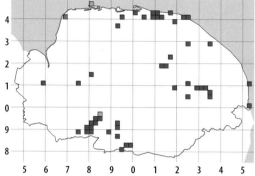

♂, Beeston Common, 1 August

- ■ **FLIGHT** April–September. Males from June.
- ■ **DISTRIBUTION** Widely distributed and common but with few records from central areas.
- ■ **HABITAT** Areas with light soils including quarries, heathland, cliffs, Brecks, chalk grassland.
- ■ **FLOWERS VISITED** Dodder, turnip.
- ■ **NESTING** A cleptoparasite of at least five *Lasioglossum* species (SF). The distribution best fits *L. leucopus* in Norfolk.

Sphecodes gibbus Dark-winged Blood Bee

Females of this large species have a wide head with several rows of punctures behind the ocelli (most *Sphecodes* lack punctures here). There are black hairs and spines on the hind tibia. The wings are darkened but the wing stigmas are pale brown. **Males** also have punctures behind the ocelli and pale wing stigmas. There are orange/red markings on T1–T3.

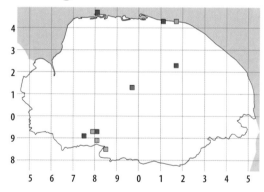

♀, Isle of Wight, 11 July [PB]

- ■ **FLIGHT** May–September with males from July.
- ■ **DISTRIBUTION** A scarce species with recent records from the Brecks, Scolt Head, Weybourne and Marsham Heath. It was described as "generally distributed, common" by Bridgman 1879.
- ■ **HABITAT** Brecks, coastal grassland, heathland.
- ■ **FLOWERS VISITED** No records.
- ■ **NESTING** A cleptoparasite of *Halictus rubicundus* (BWARS) but recorded from only a few sites of this species. Four of the ten tetrads with records of *S. gibbus* also have records of *H. rubicundus*.

Sphecodes hyalinatus Furry-bellied Blood Bee

Females: this small species resembles *Sphecodes geoffrellus* but differs in having less punctation on T2 and T3 (requiring microscopic examination) and dense white hairs under the thorax. **Males** require microscopic examination of antennae and genitalia for identification.

- **FLIGHT** May–August with males from July.
- **DISTRIBUTION** Recorded at Honing Churchyard 1996 (PY), Narborough 2002 (KD) and 2012 (TS), Foulden Common 2003 (Brecks Project) and at Warham Camp 2012 and 2016 (NO).
- **HABITAT** Calcareous grassland.
- **FLOWERS VISITED** No records.
- **NESTING** A cleptoparasite of *Lasioglossum fulvicorne* and *L. fratellum* (SF). The former species has been recorded in the same tetrad

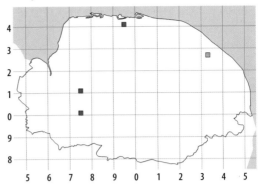

as *Sphecodes hyalinatus* at Narborough and Foulden but neither species so far at Warham Camp.

Sphecodes longulus Little Sickle-jawed Blood Bee

Females are tiny with single-pointed mandibles (otherwise seen only in *Sphecodes puncticeps*). The body is slim and the tarsi and parts of the tibiae are reddish. **Males** are very slim with pale tarsi and pale marks at each end of the tibiae. The abdomen is mostly black with variable amounts of reddish tints on T1–T3.

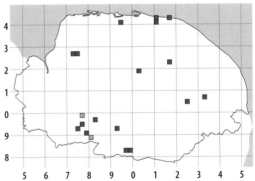

♂, Beeston Common, 25 July

- **FLIGHT** April–August. Males from July.
- **DISTRIBUTION** Widespread in the county.
- **HABITAT** Quarries, chalk grassland, heathland, Brecks.
- **FLOWERS VISITED** No records.
- **NESTING** A cleptoparasite of *Lasioglossum morio*, *L. minutissimum* and possibly other *Lasioglossum* species (SF). It is not clear from the distribution which hosts are used in Norfolk.

Sphecodes miniatus False Margined Blood Bee

Females of this small species have fairly dense punctures on the thorax and a reticulate pattern on the propodeum. They are very similar to *Sphecodes geoffrellus* (SF). **Males** require examination of genitalia to determine.

- **FLIGHT** April–September. Males from September (only one record).
- **DISTRIBUTION** Recorded in the Brecks, the Norwich area and the north coast.
- **HABITAT** Brownfield sites, quarries, cliffs, forest rides.
- **FLOWERS VISITED** Dandelion.
- **NESTING** Observed near *Lasioglossum morio* nests at Brundall (TS) which is a known host, as is *L. smeathmanellum* (SF). However, *Sphecodes*

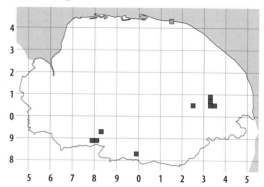

miniatus is scarce and localised in Norfolk compared with these two *Lasioglossum* species.

Sphecodes monilicornis Box-headed Blood Bee

Females of this fairly large species have rows of punctures on the head behind the ocelli. The head is squarish in shape, with the sides coming out backwards behind the eyes before curving sharply inwards. **Males** have long antennae without obvious hair patches. There are variable amounts of red on T1–T3.

- **FLIGHT** April–September. Males from July.
- **DISTRIBUTION** Widespread and common.
- **HABITAT** Gardens, commons, heathland, Brecks.
- **FLOWERS VISITED** Bramble, creeping thistle, hogweed, garden sea holly, thyme, wild carrot, yarrow.
- **NESTING** Associated with *Lasioglossum calceatum*, a known host, near Foulden (KD). Also known to parasitise *L. albipes*, *L. malachurum* and *Halictus*

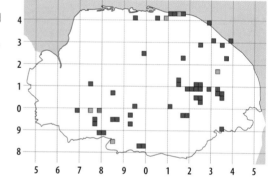

rubicundus (SF). The Norfolk distribution and abundance of *Sphecodes monilicornis* suggests that *L. calceatum* is its main host in the county.

♀ on wild thyme, Warham Camp, 5 August

♂, Beeston Common, 9 September

Sphecodes niger Dark Blood Bee

Females of this very small species can be recognised by a smooth shiny area beneath the wing base and the dark upper surface of T3.
Males are entirely black and can be mistaken for a *Lasioglossum* but have more knobbly antennae and different genitalia.

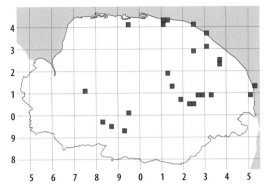

♀ on germander speedwell, showing shiny area beneath wing base, Coploe Hill, Cambridgeshire, 27 April

♀, Warham Camp, 24 May

♂, New Forest, Hampshire, 28 August [PB]

- **FLIGHT** July–September. Males from June.
- **DISTRIBUTION** Widespread in the county.
- **HABITAT** Brownfield sites, quarries, gardens, chalk grassland, Brecks.
- **FLOWERS VISITED** Milk parsley.
- **NESTING** Observed near *Lasioglossum morio* nests at Brundall (TS). This is the only reported host of *Sphecodes niger* (BWARS).

Sphecodes pellucidus Sandpit Blood Bee

Females of this fairly large species can be recognised by their wide head, large deep punctures on the thorax, wide pygidium and long white body hairs. **Males** can be identified microscopically from details of antennae and genitalia.

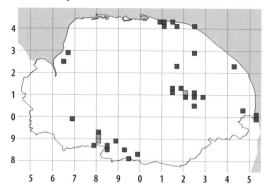

♀ excavating nest of *Andrena barbilabris*, Kelling Heath, 20 April

- **FLIGHT** Late March–September. Males from June.
- **DISTRIBUTION** Recorded from the Brecks as far west as Stoke Ferry, Roydon Common in the west, the Norwich area to the north coast, East Ruston heath and the south-east coast.
- **HABITAT** Heathland and other sites with loose unshaded sand.
- **FLOWERS VISITED** No records.
- **NESTING** A cleptoparasite of *Andrena barbilabris*. The distribution of *Sphecodes pellucidus* generally matches that of this *Andrena* in Norfolk.

Sphecodes puncticeps Sickle-jawed Blood Bee

♀, Kelling Heath, 25 May

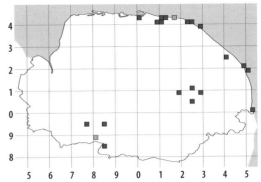

Females have a strongly punctured thorax and a wide head. The mandibles have a single point. **Males** require microscopic examination for identification.

- **FLIGHT** May–August. Males from August.
- **DISTRIBUTION** Recorded from the Brecks, the Norwich area and the north and east coasts.

- **HABITAT** Commons, heathland, quarries, cliffs and mature dunes.
- **FLOWERS VISITED** Creeping thistle, hogweed.
- **NESTING** The Norfolk distribution of *Sphecodes puncticeps* suggests that *Lasioglossum villosulum* is its main host in the county rather than the other reported hosts *L. lativentre*, *L. quadrinotatum* (SF). *L. brevicorne* may also be a host.

Sphecodes reticulatus Reticulate Blood Bee

Identification of both sexes requires examination of microscopic features. **Females** of this fairly large species have punctures behind the ocelli, as in *Sphecodes monilicornis*, but the head is not square as in that species. **Males** have long shining antennae and red markings on T2–T4.

- **FLIGHT** May–September; earliest 22 May with males from July.
- **DISTRIBUTION** Brecks, western heaths, Norwich area, Buxton Heath area, Cromer Ridge and east coast.
- **HABITAT** Heathland, coastal cliffs, Brecks.
- **FLOWERS VISITED** Yarrow.
- **NESTING** Observed investigating a nest hole of *Lasioglossum leucozonium* at Weybourne on 23 July 2012 but any association needs confirming. Reported as parasitising *Andrena barbilabris* and *A. dorsata* in Europe (BWARS). The distribution of *Sphecodes reticulatus* in Norfolk could relate to its parasitising *L. leucozonium* and/or *A. barbilabris* but probably not *A. dorsata* which is very widespread and abundant in the county. *S. reticulatus* appears about a month later than *S. pellucidus* which is a known parasite of *A. barbilabris*.

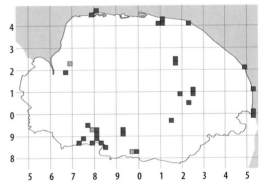

♂ on yarrow, Kelling Heath, 25 August

Sphecodes rubicundus Red-tailed Blood Bee

Females: a large species with T4 entirely red, as in *Sphecodes gibbus*, but lacking the darkened wings of that species. **Males** can be identified by details of antennae and genitalia (SF).

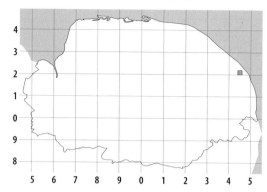

- **FLIGHT** No information.
- **DISTRIBUTION** Bridgman found it to be common in the Norwich area in the 1870s. One individual was recorded at Hickling in 1988, thought to be a vagrant, but it is possible that its host is or was still present.
- **HABITAT** No information.
- **FLOWERS VISITED** No information.
- **NESTING** Known to be a parasite of *Andrena labialis* (BWARS), which has not been recorded in the county since the 19th century.

Sphecodes spinulosus Spined Blood Bee

Both sexes of this large species can be identified microscopically by the curved flange along the hind margin of the head, resembling a narrow gutter. **Females** have long antennae, looking more like those of males and a deep groove across sternite two. **Males** have spines on the hind tibiae.

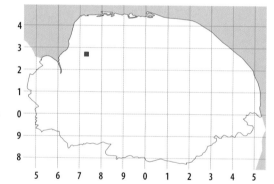

- **FLIGHT** Recorded in July.
- **DISTRIBUTION** There is only one record: a female from a chalk field headland at Flitcham on 7 July 2013 (NO confirmed GE).
- **HABITAT** Chalky fields.
- **FLOWERS VISITED** No records.
- **NESTING** Known to parasitise *Lasioglossum xanthopus* which has not been recorded in Norfolk since the 19th century but may be present at Flitcham and other chalk grassland sites.

MELITTA – BLUNTHORN BEES

The genus is represented by four species in the British Isles, three of which occur in Norfolk. All are specialised in their choice of pollen and can most easily be found by watching their food plants. They are medium-sized bees with a short tongue and can be separated from *Andrena* by their use of only the tibia and tarsus hairs to carry pollen (not significantly by the femur or propodeum), a lack of facial foveae and the swollen final segments of the tarsi. The antennae are also distinctive in having a slanting end, as if sliced diagonally with a knife.

Melitta haemorrhoidalis ♀ with purple pollen from harebell, Swanton Novers Great Wood, 16 August

Melitta haemorrhoidalis ♀ on *Campanula* sp., French Pyrenees, June

Melitta leporina ♂ on white clover, Hayling Island, Hampshire, 3 July. Note broad (orange) final tarsus joints

Melitta haemorrhoidalis Gold-tailed Melitta

Females: there are pale hairs on the face and a mixture of pale orange and dark hairs on the thorax, with dense pale hairs on the sides of the thorax and the propodeum. There are long pale hairs on T1, fine white marginal bands on T2–T4 and orange hairs at the tip of the abdomen, often visible when the bee is immersed in a flower. The hind tibia and tarsus have orange hairs with some orange hairs on other leg parts. **Males** are similar but hairier and have more obvious hair bands on the tergites. There are some orange hairs on the legs and pale orange hairs at the tip of the abdomen.

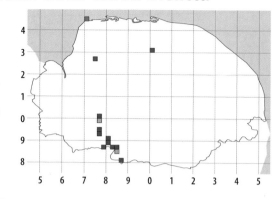

- ■ **FLIGHT** July–September
- ■ **DISTRIBUTION** Most records come from the Brecks. Recorded as 'not uncommon' round Norwich by Bridgman 1879 and seen at West Runton 1900 by Wainright. Recorded at Holme-next-the-Sea 1963 (PY), at Swanton Novers Great Wood 2015 and Flitcham 2016 (NO). These last three records were on harebell.
- ■ **HABITAT** Grasslands with harebells or other Campanulaceae.
- ■ **FLOWERS VISITED** Specialises in Campanualceae, especially harebell in Norfolk.
- ■ **NESTING** No Norfolk information.
- ■ **PARASITES** None recorded.

♀ visiting harebells, Swanton Novers Great Wood, 16 August

♂, French Pyrenees

Melitta leporina Clover Melitta

Females: there are dense pale buff hairs on the face and dark hairs on the top of the head. The thorax has a mixture of dark and pale hairs grading to paler hair on the sides. The tergites have a covering of pale buff hairs with variable amounts of black mixed in on T3–T6 and there are prominent pale marginal bands. The scopa hairs on the hind tibiae are also pale. **Males** are similar to females.

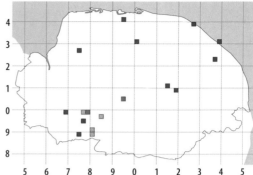

- ■ **FLIGHT** June–September.
- ■ **DISTRIBUTION** A scattering of records across the county with most coming from the Brecks.
- ■ **HABITAT** Grasslands with Fabaceae including brownfield sites, woodland rides, Brecks grasslands, soft cliffs.
- ■ **FLOWERS VISITED** Wild mignonette (male) is the only county evidence but it is known to be a specialist on Fabaceae such as clovers and vetches.
- ■ **NESTING** No Norfolk information.
- ■ **PARASITES** *Nomada flavopicta*.

♀ on white clover, Hayling Island, Hampshire, July

♂ on white clover, Hayling Island, Hampshire, July

Melitta tricincta Red Bartsia Bee

Females resemble *Melitta leporina* but the marginal bands on the abdomen are narrower and whiter. **Males** have black hairs on T2 whereas *M. leporina* has none. The strong association with red bartsia is a good clue to identity.

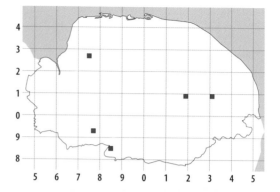

♀ on red bartsia, Flitcham, 30 August

♀ on red bartsia, Flitcham, 30 August

- **FLIGHT** July–September
- **DISTRIBUTION** The first definite county record was a male at Thetford Warren Lodge on 19 July 2009 (TS). Further records come from Bowthorpe 2013 (GN, PH), Cranwich Heath 2015, Brundall 2015 (TS) and Flitcham 2016 (NO). This last site is the most northerly record in the British Isles so far. It may be spreading northwards.
- **HABITAT** Heathland, brownfield sites, chalk grassland.
- **FLOWERS VISITED** Strongly associated with red bartsia, an annual plant which grows on heavy or compacted soils.
- **NESTING** No information.
- **PARASITES** No information.

There is one representative of this genus in the British Isles, which is present in Norfolk. It specialises on one plant species, yellow loosestrife, from which it takes floral oils as well as pollen. This is a wetland plant which is abundant in the Broads. Pollen is collected on the hind tibiae. There are two submarginal cells on the forewings and the tongue is short.

Macropis europaea Yellow Loosestrife Bee

Females have pale hair on the clypeus and a mixture of sparse dark and light hairs on the upper thorax. There are long white hairs below the wings. The abdomen is shiny with prominent white hair bands on T3 and T4. The hind tibiae have conspicuous white pollen hairs, emphasised by the black hairs of the basitarsi. **Males**: the cuticle on the face is yellow up to the level of the antennae. The body hairs are pale brown with an incomplete white hair band on T3, complete bands on T4–T6 and a black pygidium. The legs are swollen, especially the hind femur and tarsus, perhaps an adaptation used when gripping the female when mating.

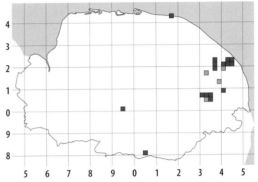

♀ on yellow loosestrife, Beeston Common, 12 August

- **FLIGHT** Late June–August.
- **DISTRIBUTION** Most records come from the northern Broads and the Yare Valley. There are outlying records from near Watton, Redgrave and Lopham Fen and from Beeston Common. It was recorded near King's Lynn by Atmore in the early 1900s.
- **HABITAT** Bogs, river valleys, fens and broads where yellow loosestrife grows.
- **FLOWERS VISITED** Females recorded on creeping thistle, yellow loosestrife, and water mint and a male on milk parsley.
- **NESTING** Nest observed on an artificial bee bank (GN). Sometimes nests in small aggregations and uses floral oils as waterproofing (BWARS).
- **PARASITES** None observed.

♂, Beeston Common, 25 July

There is one species in the British Isles, which is found in Norfolk, *Dasypoda hirtipes*. It can be distinguished from *Andrena* and *Melitta* species by the presence of two rather than three submarginal cells on the forewing. The tongue is quite short and both sexes are very hairy. They are usually seen at yellow Asteraceae flowers in sandy habitats.

Dasypoda hirtipes Pantaloon Bee

Females: the most notable feature is the very long orange hairs forming the scopa on the hind tibiae. There are pale hairs on the clypeus and some dark hairs around the antennae, with a ruff of pale hairs round the back and sides of the head. There are orange and black hairs on the upper thorax contrasting with paler hairs below. The tergites have prominent white terminal hair bands. **Males** have more uniform long orange-brown hair.

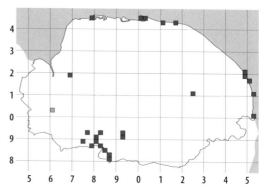

♀ digging a nest hole, Weybourne cliffs, 30 August. The hairs on the legs help to sweep away sand from the nest entrance

- **FLIGHT** July–September.
- **DISTRIBUTION** Mostly found on sandy coastal areas and the Brecks. There are single records from Laziate, Downham Market and Mousehold Heath. The species is close to the northern edge of its British range in north Norfolk. Atmore 1909 reported it as 'abundant at one locality' near King's Lynn.
- **HABITAT** Dunes, coastal marshes, Breckland forest rides, heathland, commons.
- **FLOWERS VISITED** Yellow Asteraceae including garden coneflower, cat's-ear, nipplewort, hawkweeds, ragwort.
- **NESTING** Nests in small aggregations, for example at the top of cliffs at Weybourne, where about 10 nest holes were present in late August 2015.
- **PARASITES** Cleptoparasitic flies *Miltogramma* sp.

♀ on garden coneflower, Weybourne, 24 July

♂ on fleabane, Weybourne Camp, 3 August. Note the two submarginal cells on the wing

Large, lively, broadly built bees with a long tongue and prominent yellow markings. Pollen is collected beneath the abdomen. The forewings have two submarginal cells. Males have spines on the tip of the abdomen and can be territorial. There is one British species which often comes to garden flowers, such as catmint. One species occurs in the British Isles, and is found in Norfolk.

Anthidium manicatum Wool Carder Bee

Both sexes are easily recognised by the row of yellow spots (sometimes bars) on the abdomen. There are also yellow markings on the face, legs and mandibles and a yellow spot behind each eye. The tongue is long. **Females** have broad white fore and mid tarsi covered in white hairs and yellow markings on the tibiae. The thorax has sparse brown hair and the scopa, beneath the abdomen, is whitish in colour. **Males** are larger than females and possess a row of spines at the end of the abdomen, used when attacking other insects straying into their territory. The tibiae and tarsi have yellow markings and wispy white hairs.

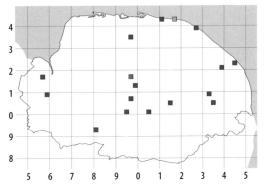

- **FLIGHT** June–August.
- **DISTRIBUTION** Widely distributed but scarce. Bridgman 1879 reports that "it abounds in mid-summer" around Norwich.
- **HABITAT** Gardens, Fenland, Broadland.
- **FLOWERS VISITED** Flowers with a deep corolla. Catmint, marsh woundwort.
- **NESTING** Hairs from the leaves of plants such as lamb's-ear are used to line the nest, which is made in a hollow stem or other cavity.
- **PARASITES** *Stelis punctulatissima*.

Mating pair, Essex [TB]

♀ (form with bars) on ground-ivy, Essex [TB]

♀ (form with spots) on catmint, Weybourne, June

Four species occur in the British Isles with three recorded in Norfolk. Members of this genus are cleptoparasites of other bees and there is no scopa. Like many cleptoparasites they have a strong, punctured cuticle. Some species have spots on the abdomen. The wings have three sub-marginal cells.

Stelis ornatula Spotted Dark Bee

Females: there are paired white spots on T1–T4 and sparse white hairs on the head and thorax, with longer pale hairs on the clypeus and beneath the wings. The abdomen is largely hairless. **Males** are very similar to females.

- ■ **FLIGHT** May–June.
- ■ **DISTRIBUTION** Two records: Cranwich Camp and Grimes graves 2011 (GN).
- ■ **HABITAT** Breckland short grassland.
- ■ **FLOWERS VISITED** No information.
- ■ **NESTING** The host is *Hoplitis claviventris* which is also confined to the Brecks in the county.

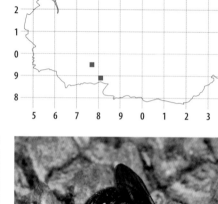

♀ at nest holes of *Hoplitis claviventris*, Devil's Dyke, Cambridgeshire, 24 June

♀ at nest holes of *Hoplitis claviventris*, Devil's Dyke, Cambridgeshire, 24 June

Stelis phaeoptera Plain Dark Bee

♀, Shropshire [AJ]

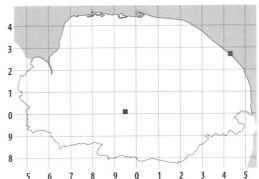

Females: there is sparse white body hair with inconspicuous lateral hair bands on the abdomen but no pale spots. There are no pollen hairs and the cuticle is heavily punctured. **Males** are similar to females.

- ■ **FLIGHT** June–August.
- ■ **DISTRIBUTION** One was recorded by Bridgman at Brundall on thistles 10 August 1879. There is a specimen of a female in the Natural History Museum from Waxham 9 August 1936

collected at a holes in a poplar tree thought to be occupied by *Megachile willughbiella* and/or *Osmia leaiana* (presumably the latter) but the collector is not recorded. The only subsequent county records are from a large garden near Watton where a male was recorded in 2008 and a male and a female in 2011. All were on an artificial bee wall in June (GN).

- ■ **HABITAT** As for the host, *Osmia leaiana*.
- ■ **FLOWERS VISITED** No information.
- ■ **NESTING** A cleptoparasite on *Osmia leaiana*.

Stelis punctulatissima Banded Dark Bee

Females have sparse pale body hairs and pale hind margins to the tergites. The body is covered in conspicuous punctures and the wings are darkened. **Males** are similar to females.

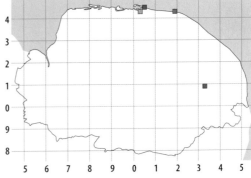

♀ on garden coneflower, Cley, 9 August [MF]

- ■ **FLIGHT** June–July.
- ■ **DISTRIBUTION** Recorded in Bridgman's garden in Norwich in July in the late 1800s, at West Runton in 1900 where Wainright described it as "not uncommon on Bramble blossoms", a female at Wiveton Downs in July 1997 (PY), a female in a Brundall garden in 2006 and 2007 (TS) and a female in a Cley garden 2012 (MF).
- ■ **HABITAT** As for *Anthidium manicatum*.
- ■ **FLOWERS VISITED** Bramble, garden coneflower.
- ■ **NESTING** A cleptoparasite of *Anthidium manicatum*.

One member of the genus occurs in Norfolk and is a recent arrival. A second species has been recorded in Dorset, probably as a vagrant. These bees are 5-6 mm in length and can be recognised by the habit of dipping their abdomen up and down as they brush pollen onto the scopa, which is beneath the abdomen, often from a yellow Asteraceae flower such as ragwort. The wings have two sub-marginal cells. The genus is characterised partly by a transverse ridge near the front edge of T1, though this is hard to see in a photograph.

Heriades truncorum Large-headed Resin Bee

Females: the large head has a patch of flattened hairs at the inner edge of each eye and there are also pale hairs on the thorax and pale hair bands on the rather narrow abdomen. The scopa is orange. **Males** look similar to females but the tip of their abdomen is curled under.

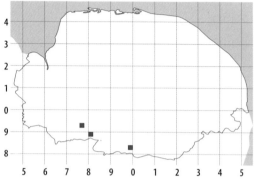

Heriades sp. ♀ on *Inula* sp., Mallorca, 26 September

- **FLIGHT** August.
- **DISTRIBUTION** A southern species first recorded in the county in 2012 at Middle Harling Heath. Also recorded at Cranwich Heath and Santon Warren 2015 (all TS).
- **HABITAT** Grassy heathland with dead wood for nesting.
- **FLOWERS VISITED** Ragwort.
- **NESTING** Uses holes in wood made by other insects such as beetle larvae. Resin is collected and used for making cell partitions and sealing the nest hole. Colony in a dead pine stump Middle Harking Heath (TS).
- **PARASITES** *Stelis breviuscula* but this has not yet been recorded in Norfolk.

Heriades sp. ♀ collecting resin, Mallorca, 19 October

Heriades sp. takes resin from store at nest entrance, Mallorca, October

Small narrow bees with a scopa beneath the abdomen. The wings have two submarginal cells. Males have a pair of projections on the tip of T7. Two species occur in the British Isles, both occurring in Norfolk.

Chelostoma campanularum Small Scissor Bee

Females: slender black bees with sparse white hairs and a white scopa with a rounded tip to the abdomen. There are no hair bands on the tergites. **Males** are similar but lack a scopa and have a pair of slender projections on T7.

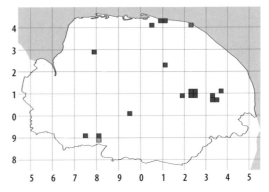

- ■ **FLIGHT** June–August.
- ■ **DISTRIBUTION** Widely distributed but absent from the Broads and Fens where their host plants may be scarce. It is near the northern edge of its British range in north Norfolk.
- ■ **HABITAT** Gardens, woodland rides, grasslands.
- ■ **FLOWERS VISITED** Specialist on bellflowers (Campanulaceae) but also recorded on yellow Asteraceae, garden geranium and wild carrot.
- ■ **NESTING** Uses holes in wood and masonry, including bee hotels.
- ■ **PARASITES** None observed.

♀, Thriplow, Cambridgeshire, 19 July

♀ on garden geranium seemingly with geranium pollen, Weybourne, 3 August

♂, Weybourne, 27 July

Chelostoma florisomne Large Scissor Bee

♀ at nest hole, Strumpshaw Fen [TS]

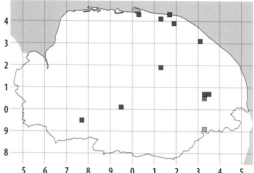

♀ at nest hole, Strumpshaw Fen [TS]

Females: much larger than the previous species. The mandibles are long and curved. There are white hairs on the body including the scopa. T1 and T2 have widely interrupted white marginal hair bands but on T3 and T4 they are complete. **Males** resemble females but have square ended projections on T7.

- ■ **FLIGHT** May–August.
- ■ **DISTRIBUTION** Widely distributed but seemingly scarce in the county.
- ■ **HABITAT** Gardens, woodland clearings, river valleys.
- ■ **FLOWERS VISITED** No Norfolk information. Pollen is taken from buttercups in which the bee sometimes rests in cool weather (SF).
- ■ **NESTING** Nests in a variety of holes and cavities including bee hotels.
- ■ **PARASITES** Thought to include the wasp *Monosapyga clavicornis* (SF).

♀ on buttercup, Furzey Gardens, New Forest, Hampshire [PC]

♂, Furzey Gardens, New Forest, Hampshire [PC]

Twelve species of *Osmia* occur in the British Isles with six recorded in Norfolk, including the familiar Red Mason Bee *Osmia bicornis*, and a seventh unconfirmed. Nests are made in various cavities including hollow stems, 'bee hotels' and, in one species, snail shells. The cells are sealed with either mud or leaf mastic. Those species using mastic have a large head containing the necessary muscles for chewing leaves. The wings have two sub-marginal cells. Pollen is collected in a scopa (pollen brush) below the abdomen: the colour of the scopa can assist in identification. The tongue is quite long enabling flowers with a deep corolla to be used. Males tend to return often to the same basking spots. As with many bee species, the bright colours of newly hatched individuals quickly fade to grey, making identification more difficult. *Osmia* and *Megachile* are good groups to start with if you are new to bees.

Osmia caerulescens ♀ collecting leaf material for nest, Weybourne, 13 July

Osmia bicornis ♂ seeks nectar in ground-ivy, Swanton Novers, May

Osmia caerulescens ♀ (black scopa) on *Cistus* sp., Cambridge, 12 June

Osmia leaiana ♀ (orange scopa), Roydon Common, 18 July

Osmia aurulenta Gold-fringed Mason Bee

Females have large heads with large mandibles and a long tongue and the eyes have greenish flecks. Much of the body has a covering of sparse bright orange hair. The abdomen has narrow pale hair bands and the scopa beneath the abdomen is also orange. The cuticle is black. **Males** are similar to females. There are notches at the sides of tergite 6 (absent in *Osmia bicolor*).

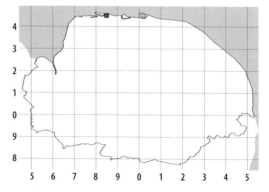

♀, Pembrey, Carmarthenshire, Wales, 11 July

♂, Pembrey, Carmarthenshire, Wales, 11 July

- **FLIGHT** Recorded in July.
- **DISTRIBUTION** Reported from Gun Hill, Holkham in July 2001 but no details given (NBN). This is a likely habitat but Its presence needs confirmation.
- **HABITAT** Dunes.

- **FLOWERS VISITED** No information.
- **NESTING** No records: often makes nest in an empty snail shell (BWARS).
- **PARASITES** The wasp *Sapyga quinquepunctata* (BWARS).

Osmia bicolor Red-tailed Mason Bee

Females have black hair on the head and thorax and orange hairs on the abdomen. The scopa hairs are orange. The cuticle of the hind tibia is orange. **Males** have pale hairs on the clypeus and orange hairs on most other parts of the body. The tip of the abdomen is evenly rounded.

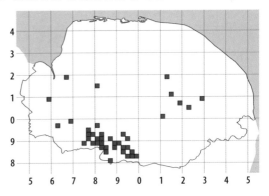

- **FLIGHT** March–June.
- **DISTRIBUTION** Abundant in the Brecks and recently spreading from that area. Recorded at Narborough Railway Line 2010, Alderford Common 2010, Cringleford 2011, Bawsey 2012, Norwich Hall Road 2012, Stoke Ferry 2012, Castle Acre, Roudham, Wymondham and Queen's Hills in 2014. These records represent the current northerly limit of this species in the British Isles. It has not yet been found in a study of chalk grassland near Flitcham.
- **HABITAT** Usually nests on fairly bare gravelly ground in chalky habitats where empty snail shells remain on the surface.
- **FLOWERS VISITED** Crab apple, dandelion, other yellow Asteraceae, hawthorn, mahonia.
- **NESTING** Nests are made inside empty snail shells. The compartment(s) are sealed with leaf mastic and mineral grains. The female covers the completed nest with grass stems which are carried in flight and dropped onto the sealed shell, making a small wigwam. A nest at West Tofts was in the shell of *Cepaea* sp.
- **PARASITES** None observed.

♀ investigates a snail shell *Cepaea* sp. for her nest [PC]

♀ on bird's-foot-trefoil, Kent, 10 June

♂, West Tofts, March

Osmia bicornis (*O. rufa*) Red Mason Bee

Females have two short horns on the face between the eye and the base of the mandible which are not present in any other British *Osmia* species. The clypeal hairs are pale but there is black hair between the antennae and on top of the head. The thorax has pale hair and the abdomen bright orange hair, giving the species its common name. The scopa is also orange. The cuticle looks metallic where it shines through the hair. **Males** have a similar colour pattern to females but have less black hair on the head. The antennae are very long.

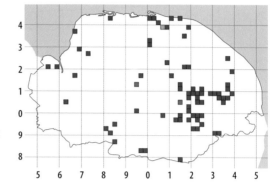

- **FLIGHT** March–early July.
- **DISTRIBUTION** Widespread and fairly common, including in built up areas.
- **HABITAT** Gardens, churchyards, woodland rides and glades, river valleys, commons.
- **FLOWERS VISITED** Alkanet, apple, blackthorn, bluebell, bramble, bugle, catmint, cistus, dandelion, forget-me-not, ground-ivy, mallow, poppy, raspberry, rhododendron, rosemary, speedwells, thyme.
- **NESTING** Makes a linear series of nest chambers separated by mud partitions in hollow stems, holes in walls or sandy banks.
- **PARASITES** The wasp *Sapyga quinquepunctata* and the fly *Drosophila indagator*.

♀ and ♂, Weybourne, 13 May

♂ at nest hole, Brokenhurst, Hampshire [PB]

Osmia caerulescens Blue Mason Bee

Females: the head is large and square with a long tongue. There is white hair on the clypeus and thorax and white hair bands on the margins of the tergites. The scopa hairs are black which is unique in Norfolk's *Osmia* species. **Males** are very different from females, with orange hair on the head, thorax and abdomen. The cuticle is slightly metallic.

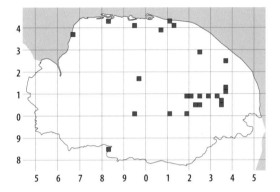

♀ on garden lobelia, Weybourne, 8 August. Note the black scopa with some yellow pollen

♂, Weybourne, 21 June

- **FLIGHT** March–July.
- **DISTRIBUTION** Widespread in the county but apparently absent from the Brecks, though one record near Watton. Not recorded from the Fens or on the coast.
- **HABITAT** Gardens, river valleys, churchyards, old railway tracks, parkland.
- **FLOWERS VISITED** Catmint, forget-me-not, germander speedwell, ivy-leaved toadflax, garden Jacob's ladder, garden lobelia, meadow saxifrage, ramsons, scabious, woundwort.
- **NESTING** In bamboo and brick holes in a Brundall garden, 12 June 2006 (TS).
- **PARASITES** None observed.

Osmia leaiana Orange-vented Mason Bee

Females: the head is large and there are prominent punctures on the head and thorax. There is pale hair on the face and thorax and pale marginal bands on the abdomen. The scopa is bright orange, fading to pale orange in older individuals. The wings are darkened. **Males** have a tuft of prominent pale hairs on the clypeus, orange hairs on the thorax and pale marginal bands of longish hairs on the abdomen. The cuticle is only slightly metallic.

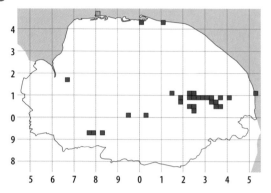

♀ on garden geranium, Weybourne, 13 June

♂, Cambridge, 25 June

- **FLIGHT** May–early September.
- **DISTRIBUTION** Common in the Norwich area with a scattering of records elsewhere.
- **HABITAT** Gardens, quarries, Breckland, heathland, dunes, churchyards.
- **FLOWERS VISITED** Yellow Asteraceae, creeping cinquefoil, fleabane (pollen), greater knapweed, black knapweed, purple-loosestrife, spear thistle, marsh thistle.

- **NESTING** Sealing a completed nest with leaf mastic in a bee hotel (bamboo), Weybourne, 2 August 2012. Seen entering a hole in a sandy bank on Kelling Heath, 14 August 2009.
- **PARASITES** *Stelis phaeoptera* and the wasp *Chrysura radians* (BWARS).

Osmia pilicornis Fringe-horned Mason Bee

One record from King's Lynn by Atmore 1899.

Osmia spinulosa Spined Mason Bee

Females: this is a small species. There are pale brown hairs on the clypeus and thorax and pale marginal hair bands on the abdomen. The scopa is pale orange and the eyes are blue-green.
Males resemble females in colouration. They possess a large forward facing spine beneath the abdomen, which is diagnostic but not easy to see. The final tarsus joints are orange.

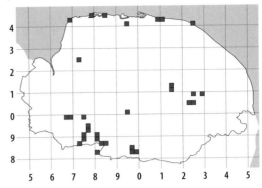

- **FLIGHT** June–September.
- **DISTRIBUTION** Mostly recorded in the Brecks, the Norwich area and the north coast. This is close to the northern edge of its British range.
- **HABITAT** Calcareous Brecks, quarries, dunes, gardens, chalk grassland.
- **FLOWERS VISITED** Black knapweed, ragwort, scabious, yellow Asteraceae.
- **NESTING** No Norfolk information.
- **PARASITES** Uses empty snail shells (BWARS).

♀, Cranwich, 16 July

♂ on field scabious, Weybourne Camp, 9 July

Mating pair, Warham Camp, 19 June

This genus is very similar to *Osmia* and can be distinguished mainly by fine details of the markings on the thorax, not easily visible in a photograph. The wings have two sub-marginal cells. Two species occur in the British Isles, one a recent arrival. One species occurs in Norfolk.

Hoplitis claviventris Welted Mason Bee

Females: the cuticle is black with pale brown hairs on the clypeus and upper thorax. There are long white hairs beneath the wings and white marginal hair bands on the abdomen. The scopa has pale hairs. **Males**: the eyes have a greenish tint. There are pale hairs on the clypeus and brown hairs on the top of the head and thorax, with brownish-white marginal hair bands on the abdomen.

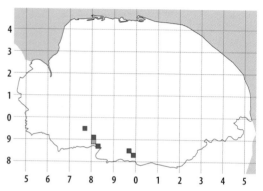

♀, Cranwich, 6 July

♀ at nest hole, Cambridgeshire, June

- ■ **FLIGHT** June–July.
- ■ **DISTRIBUTION** Modern records come only from the Brecks but Atmore 1909 reports nine individuals (as *Osmia leucomelana*) on Bird's-foot Trefoil near King's Lynn.
- ■ **HABITAT** Breckland forest rides and open grasslands including Grimes Graves.

- ■ **FLOWERS VISITED** Favours Fabaceae such as birds's-foot-trefoil.
- ■ **NESTING** Nests in (vertical) hollow stems, holes in the ground and in wood and a variety of other cavities. The nest partitions are made with leaf mastic.
- ■ **NESTING** *Stelis ornatula* is a cleptoparasite.

The mandibles of these bees work like scissors to cut pieces out of leaves or petals to form their nests. Several species make their nests in crevices or holes in timber whereas others use holes in sandy ground. Those requiring timber tend to be absent from the coastal strip, whereas those which nest in the ground often have a coastal bias in their distribution. All have two submarginal cells on the forewing and the tongue is quite long. Their name comes from the long tarsal claws which lack an ariolum (small pad) between. Their characteristic posture, with tail in the air on alighting, makes these bees easy to spot.

Megachile centuncularis ♀ cutting a rose leaf, Oxford, April [PC]

It is often possible to identify Leaf-cutter Bees from good photographs. The scopa hairs beneath the abdomen differ in colour between species, but the scopa needs to be seen without pollen. Males can be distinguished from females by the male's lack of a scopa and their longer antennae. They emerge about a week earlier than females and for the first few days, before it fades, their hair is bright ginger-brown. The males of three species have distinctive white swellings on the front tarsi and the male of another species has very green eyes. Bees in the genus *Coelioxys* are brood parasites of *Megachile*. There are seven species of *Megachile* in the British Isles, all of which occur in Norfolk.

Megachile centuncularis ♀

Megachile leachella ♂ on bird's-foot-trefoil, Holkham, June. The two submarginal cells are visible on the left wing

Megachile centuncularis Patchwork Leafcutter Bee

Females have pale hair on the clypeus and thorax, but there are some dark hairs on top of the head. The abdomen has pale marginal bands at the edges of tergites 1–5, with hair length decreasing from T1–T5. There are bands of sparser, longer hairs on T1 and T2. The scopa is entirely orange and the hairs protrude outwards making them visible from above. **Males** have pale hair on the clypeus and a mixture of dark and pale hairs on the top of the head and thorax. The abdomen bears similar marginal bands to those in females.

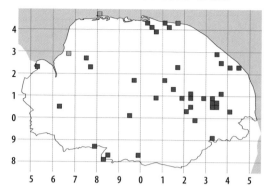

♀ taking nectar from a garden coneflower, Weybourne, 2 August

- **FLIGHT** June–August.
- **DISTRIBUTION** One of the commonest leafcutters in the county, but there are few records from the west. Scarce on the coast, though reported from Scolt Head.
- **HABITAT** Heathland, commons, gardens, waysides, Breckland rides.
- **FLOWERS VISITED** Alkanet, bird's-foot-trefoil, bramble, crown daisy, fleabane, green coneflower, hemp-agrimony, lamb's-ear, black knapweed, meadow crane's-bill, meadow vetchling, purple-loosestrife, ragwort, rosebay willowherb.
- **NESTING** Nests are made in a variety of cavities in wood, buildings or hollow stems, including 'bee hotels'. Rose leaves or petals are often used in gardens.
- **PARASITES** *Coelioxys inermis*.

♂ on garden marigold, Weybourne, 3 July

♀ taking nectar from rosebay willowherb, Weybourne, 5 August

Megachile circumcincta Black-headed Leafcutter Bee

Females: the general body hair is long. The hairs on the face are dark brown-black and black on the top of the head. The thorax hairs are sparse and red-brown. The hairs are also black on T4–6. The scopa is brown at the base and black at the tip. **Males** have white clypeal hairs and a small expanded white area of cuticle on the front tarsi.

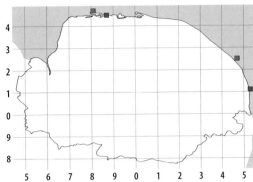

♀ on bird's-foot-trefoil, Holkham Dunes, 19 June

- **FLIGHT** May–August.
- **DISTRIBUTION** This is the rarest Leafcutter in the county and it has declined nationally. There are recent records from dunes at Caister 2007 and at Great Yarmouth 2015 (TS) and from Holkham Dunes where 2–3 females were observed visiting Bird's-foot-trefoil in June 2016 (NO). There are also records from Horsey Dunes 1958, Scolt Head 1975 and from the Brecks 1998. It was described as being "not uncommon round the city in June-July" by Bridgman in the late 19th century.
- **HABITAT** Coastal dunes.
- **FLOWERS VISITED** Bird's-foot-trefoil in very fast flight.
- **NESTING** Nests in sandy ground. Not observed in Norfolk.
- **PARASITES** *Coelioxys* spp.

♀ on bird's-foot-trefoil, Holkham Dunes, 19 June

Megachile leachella Silvery Leafcutter Bee

Females have pale body hairs with a tint of brown on the head and top of the thorax. There are complete white marginal bands on all tergites and a characteristic pair of white hair patches on the last tergite. The small size of this species is also a clue to identification. **Males** have white hair on the clypeus and orange-brown hair on the top of the head, thorax and abdomen. There are complete marginal white bands on the tergites. T6 has a covering of pale hairs and bears short terminal spines. The eyes are a vivid pale green. They are often observed basking on sandy ground close to nest sites.

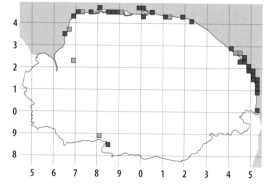

♀ on wild mignonette, Weybourne Camp, 12 August

♀ entering nest hole, Weybourne, August

♂ showing green eyes, Holkham, 8 June

- ■ **FLIGHT** June–September.
- ■ **DISTRIBUTION** This is largely a coastal species, but there is a record from Roydon Common 1996 and one from Santon Warren 1986 and from Thetford Warren Lodge 2016 (TS).
- ■ **HABITAT** Sites with loose sand or sand dunes where small sandy cliffs are present for nesting. The north-east cliff faces are not used but places with loose sand at the cliff-top can be, for example West Runton beach car park.
- ■ **FLOWERS VISITED** Greater bird's-foot-trefoil, bramble, cat's-ear, charlock, Brassicaeae sp., fleabane, hare's-foot clover, hawkweed, heather (ling), Oxford ragwort, ragwort, restharrow, sheep's-bit, wild mignonette.
- ■ **NESTING** Nests are made individually on sloping or level sandy surfaces.
- ■ **PARASITES** A small form of *Coelioxys mandibularis* attacks this species in large dune systems on the coasts of Kent, Sussex, South Wales and Lancashire but it has not been recorded in Norfolk.

Megachile ligniseca Wood-carving Leafcutter Bee

Females are large with pale brown hair on the clypeus and thorax and black hair on the top of the head. There are long pale hairs on T1 and T2 and pale marginal bands. The scopa is white anteriorly, grading to pale orange at the back. The dark hairs on the surface of the last tergite are flattened against the body and the tip of the abdomen has a small indent. **Males** have pale hairs on the clypeus, pale brown hairs on the top of the head and thorax and pale marginal bands on the abdomen consisting of moderately long hairs. The abdomen is almost parallel sided and has a notch at the tip.

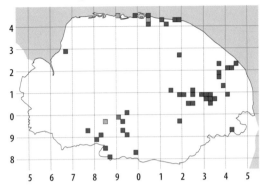

- **FLIGHT** June–September.
- **DISTRIBUTION** Moderately common in the east, the north coast and in the Brecks.
- **HABITAT** Commons, heathland, river valleys, mature dunes, gardens, open Breckland and brownfield sites.
- **FLOWERS VISITED** Garden aster, bramble, burdock, creeping thistle, dandelion, field scabious, fleabane, bell heather, black knapweed, melancholy thistle, purple-loosestrife, restharrow, perennial sowthistle, spear thistle.
- **NESTING** Nests in hollows in wood or stems, sometimes in 'bee hotels'.
- **PARASITES** *Coelioxys elongata* observed at a garden nest site in Cambridgeshire.

♀, Thriplow, Cambridgeshire, 11 August

♂, Thriplow, Cambridgeshire, 28 June

♀ taking nectar from restharrow, Weybourne Camp, 27 June

Megachile maritima Coast Leafcutter Bee

Females are large and broad with brownish hairs on the clypeus and thorax and variable amounts of black hair on the head, thorax and abdomen. The scopa has whitish hairs. **Males** are large and broad with ginger-brown hair when fresh. The fore tarsi are expanded with a white cuticle fringed by white hairs. The hind tibia and tarsus are swollen. Males move rapidly from flower to flower and sometimes defend territories.

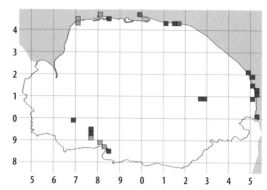

- **FLIGHT** June–August.
- **DISTRIBUTION** A coastal species also occurring at sandy inland sites near Norwich and in the Brecks.
- **HABITAT** Coastal dunes and inland sites with bare sand.
- **FLOWERS VISITED** Bird's-foot-trefoil, narrow-leaved bird's-foot-trefoil, bramble, perennial sowthistle, hare's-foot clover, sheep's-bit, restharrow, ragwort, viper's-bugloss, greater knapweed.
- **NESTING** Nests are made in the ground. On Scolt Head nests are made from privet and bramble leaves and from poplar on Blakeney Point. Males roost on flower heads such as sea holly (EAE).
- **PARASITES** *Coelioxys conoidea*.

♀, Dorset [SF]

♂ on bramble, Weybourne Camp, 9 July

♂ (faded), grooming antenna, Winterton Dunes, 17 August 2015. This bee repeatedly returned to the stem from which he launched attacks on other bees when they alighted on nearby bramble flowers. His targets included bumblebees which he clung to as the pair fell to the ground

Megachile versicolor Brown-footed Leafcutter Bee

Females are similar in size and appearance to *Megachile centuncularis* but slimmer. The scopa is orange but with contrasting dark hairs on sternites 5 and 6. The marginal bands on the abdomen are less prominent than in *M. centuncularis* and the hairs on T6 are flattened against the body rather than being erect. **Males** are also very similar to *M. centuncularis* and need microscopic examination of the sternites to separate. They have more reddish apical tarsal segments (SF).

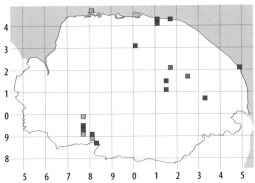

- **FLIGHT** Late May–August.
- **DISTRIBUTION** Widespread but not common.
- **HABITAT** Found in areas of flowery grassland with scrub, including mature dunes such as Scolt Head and Winterton. It also occurs in woodland rides including Swanton Novers Great Wood and shrubby heathland such as Kelling Heath and Beeston Common.
- **FLOWERS VISITED** Alkanet, bird's-foot-trefoil, creeping thistle, meadow vetchling, spear thistle. Observed collecting Asteraceae pollen, Beeston Common, August 2016
- **NESTING** Nesting on a sandy bank on Beeston Common 25th July 2016. Sometimes uses hollow stems (SF).
- **PARASITES** *Coelioxys inermis* is known to be a cleptoparasite.

♀ on spear thistle, Kelling Heath, 15 August

Megachile versicolor (probably) ♂ on alkanet, Kelling Heath, 29 June

♀ entering nest hole in bank, Beeston Common, 2 August

Megachile willughbiella Willughby's Leafcutter Bee

Females are large and broad with brownish hair. They differ from *Megachile maritima* in generally having less dark hair on the thorax and abdomen. Both have erect hairs on T6. The scopa is pale orange but there are black hairs around the edge and on the last two segments, visible from above. *M. ligniseca* differs in usually being larger with flat hairs on T6 with a notch at the end, and has few or no black hairs on the end or edge of the scopa.
Males have a modified front tibia and tarsus, similar to that of male *M. maritima* but not so large and they lack a swollen hind tibia. The hair colour of the upper parts of the body is ginger-brown.

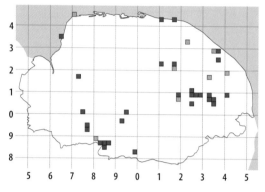

♀ on garden sweet pea, Weybourne, 20 July

♀ on borage, Weybourne, 6 September

♂ on garden speedwell, East Ruston Vicarage Garden, 20 June

- **FLIGHT** June–September.
- **DISTRIBUTION** Widespread and fairly common.
- **HABITAT** Heathland, commons, gardens, river valleys, Breckland.
- **FLOWERS VISITED** Bird's-foot-trefoil, borage, bramble, garden sweet pea, harebell, everlasting-pea, garden speedwell, field scabious.
- **NESTING** Uses a wide variety of cavities (SF).
- **PARASITES** *Coelioxys* spp..

Bees in this genus are all cleptoparasites and do not possess a scopa. The face has a mixture of pale hairs and dark bristles and the eyes are hairy. The thorax has pale brown hairs fading to white in older specimens. The wings have two submarginal cells. The abdomen has prominent wedge-shaped white hair bands. In females the abdomen tapers to a point and the tip is used to cut into the host's nest, usually a leafcutter bee. Males have spines on the tip of their more rounded abdomen. Members of this genus generally need microscopic study to confirm identification. These bees are difficult to spot because they spend a lot of time waiting near nest sites for an opportunity to enter. The area around bee hotels is a good place to look for them. Descriptions below are for females only except for *Coelioxys rufescens* which may be recogniseable. Six species have been recorded from the British Isles mainland, five species in Norfolk, one of them rare and one unrecorded for a long time.

Coelioxys sp. ♀ inspecting nests of *Megachile ligniseca*, Thriplow, Cambridgeshire, 11 August.
Partially completed nests seem to be targeted.

Coelioxys elongata ♀ showing pointed tip of abdomen, Thriplow, Cambridgeshire, 24 July

Coelioxys sp. ♂ on *Geranium* sp., Cambridge Botanic Garden, June

Coelioxys conoidea Large Sharp-tail Bee

♀ on sea holly, August [PB]

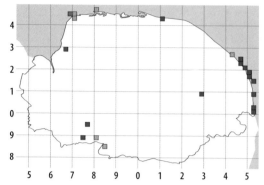

Females have pale hairs on the face and a ridge between the antennae. The hairs on the thorax are rusty brown when fresh. The abdomen has a conical tip, wider than in other *Coeloxys* species.

- ■ **FLIGHT** July–August.
- ■ **DISTRIBUTION** Recorded from the north and east coasts, near Norwich and in the Brecks. This distribution closely matches that of its host, *Megachile maritima*.
- ■ **HABITAT** As for *Megachile maritima*.
- ■ **FLOWERS VISITED** Hawkweed, knapweed, sea holly.
- ■ **NESTING** Parasitic on *Megachile maritima*.

Coelioxys elongata Dull-vented Sharp-tail Bee

♀, Thriplow, Cambridgeshire, 24 July

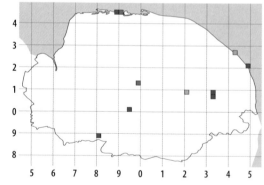

Females: the paired white abdominal marks are joined by a narrow white band and the tip (6th sternite) of the abdomen is narrower than in *Coelioxys conoidea* with tiny lateral teeth. Their shape is more elongated than *C. inermis* and the head appears relatively smaller.

- ■ **FLIGHT** June–August.
- ■ **DISTRIBUTION** Widespread but few records and probably under-recorded.
- ■ **HABITAT** Sites include gardens, commons, coastal dunes and Breckland rides.
- ■ **FLOWERS VISITED** Bramble, fleabane.
- ■ **NESTING** A parasite of *Megachile willughbiella* and *M. circumcincta*. Records from coastal dunes may relate to the latter.

Coelioxys inermis Shiny-vented Sharp-tail Bee

♀ on garden coneflower, Weybourne, 2 August

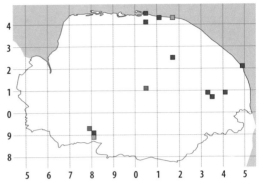

Females are very similar to *Coelioxys elongata*. There are differences in the punctation and shape of the sternites but these are unlikely to be visible in a photograph. The bee appears more compact with a broader head than *C. elongata*.

■ **FLIGHT** July–August.

■ **DISTRIBUTION** Broadly matches its main host *Megachile centuncularis*, but few records.
■ **HABITAT** Commons, gardens, river valleys, Brecks.
■ **FLOWERS VISITED** Bramble, garden coneflower, purple-loosestrife.
■ **NESTING** Parasitises a range of *Megachile* species, especially *M. centuncularis* and *M. versicolor* (SF).

Coelioxys quadridentata Grooved Sharp-tail Bee

Females can be identified by the even width of the abdominal stripes (not narrowing centrally) and by details of the 6th sternite (SF).

■ **DISTRIBUTION** The only county records are from Bridgman in the late 19th century who described

it as "not uncommon Eaton and Postwick" and also recorded it at Great Yarmouth and Bawsey Heath. It is a cleptoparasite of *Anthophora quadrimaculata* which survives in Norwich and it is quite likely that *Coelioxys quadridentata* is still present.

Coelioxys rufescens Rufescent Sharp-tail Bee

Females have a broad ended tip to the abdomen (6th sternite) and lack bristles amongst the facial hair (BWARS). **Males**: bands on the tergites show little or no central narrowing and there are four spines on the tip of the abdomen.

■ **FLIGHT** June–July.
■ **DISTRIBUTION** There are only four Norfolk records, the first being by Bridgman in Norwich

in the late 1800s. The others come from the Hickling area in 1993, the Brecks in 2003 and from Cranwich in 2008.

■ **HABITAT** Breckland heath (Cranwich) is the only identifiable Norfolk habitat. The bee was visiting a hole in a tree stump (GN).
■ **FLOWERS VISITED** No information.
■ **NESTING** A parasite of *Anthophora bimaculata* and *A. furcata* as well as *Megachile willughbiella* (SF).

♀, Malton, Yorkshire, 15 July

♂, Cambridge Botanic Garden, 25 June

Nomad Bees are often seen in low wandering flight seeking the nests of their hosts. All are cleptoparasites of other bees, laying eggs in their nests and exploiting the pollen reserves collected by the host. The Nomad Bee larva kills the host egg or larva at an early stage. The host is often an *Andrena* but can be of other genera such as *Lasioglossum* and *Melitta*. The flowers used by Nomad Bees often match those used by the host. Since Nomad Bees collect no pollen they are mostly not very hairy, and their cuticle is brightly coloured, often with wasp-like black and yellow markings. There is quite a lot of variation within each species, partly because some species use more than one host. There can also be differences between first and second generations in one season. Some can be identified from good images or even in the field, but others are very difficult to separate. Attendance at the nests of a particular host can give a useful clue, and there can be large numbers of Nomad Bees around *Andrena* nesting aggregations. There are 35 species in the British Isles of which 24 have been recorded in Norfolk, but four have not been seen in the county since the 19th century. Spring is the best time to find a range of species, but some appear later in the season.

Nomada fabriciana ♀ searching for nests of *Andrena bicolor*, Cambridge, 23 March

Nomada goodeniana ♀ looks into an *Andrena* nest hole, Kelling Heath

Nomada rufipes ♀ exploring a nest hole, Kelling Heath, August

A ♂ *Nomada rufipes* keeps watch for ♀s

Nomada argentata Silver-sided Nomad Bee

Females: the tegula and pronotal tubercles are red, as is the abdomen, which has no yellow markings. There are prominent tufts of white hair on the propodeum and sides of the abdomen and the wings are darkened. **Males** are similar but darker and largely lack red markings on the face or thorax.

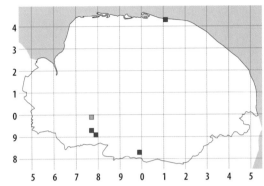

♀ on field scabious, King's Forest, Suffolk, August [TB]

♂ on field scabious, King's Forest, Suffolk, August [TB]

- **FLIGHT** Norfolk records on 5, 8 and 9 August.
- **DISTRIBUTION** Recorded on Foulden Common 1983 (AI), Weeting 2009 (GN), Weybourne Camp 2015 (NO) and at Cranwich Heath and Middle Harling Heath 2016 (TS). Seemingly scarce but probably overlooked.

- **HABITAT** Chalk grassland with scabious.
- **FLOWERS VISITED** Field scabious.
- **NESTING** A cleptoparasite of *Andrena marginata*.

Nomada armata Armed Nomad Bee

Females: this is a large species. There are red markings on the face and the thorax has red pronotal tubercles, tegula and scutellar tubercles on a black background. The abdomen is red with large yellow side markings on T2–T4 and an orange patch on T5. The antennae are bi-coloured. There are tufts of white hairs under the wings and on the propodeum. **Males** are similar but with entirely orange antennae and black scutellar tubercles.

- **FLIGHT** July–August.
- **DISTRIBUTION** Three females were recorded by Bridgman at Eaton in July 1876 but there are no subsequent records. It is possible that it still survives in the Brecks.
- **HABITAT** Presumed to be chalk grassland with scabious.
- **FLOWERS VISITED** No Norfolk information. Field scabious on Salisbury Plain.
- **NESTING** A cleptoparasite of *Andrena hattorfiana*.

♀, Salisbury Plain, Wiltshire, 11 July

♂, Salisbury Plain, Wiltshire, 11 July

Nomada baccata Bear-clawed Nomad Bee

♀, Suffolk [TB]

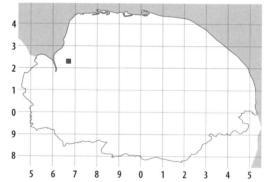

Females have a red-brown background colour. There is a black mark around the ocelli and black lines on the thorax. The abdomen has a pair of cream wedges on T2 and T3 with cream bars on T4 and T5. The legs and antennae are orange. **Males** are similar but have darker antennae and legs.

- **FLIGHT** July–September.
- **DISTRIBUTION** The first county record was at Roydon Common in August 2016 (NO, TB) though it is likely that the species has been present but overlooked for many decades.
- **HABITAT** Heathland with heather (ling) with areas of open dry sand.
- **FLOWERS VISITED** No information but likely to be heather.
- **NESTING** A cleptoparasite of *Andrena argentata*.

Nomada fabriciana Fabricius' Nomad Bee

Females: the head and thorax are largely black. The abdomen is red with a yellow spot at the side of T2 and a smaller or indistinct one on T3, though spots are absent in some dark forms. The basal antenna segments are orange followed by a zone of black segments with the final one being orange, often with a bright yellow tip. **Males** are similar to females, but with antennae largely dark.

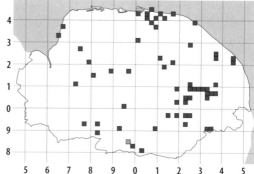

♀ on ragwort, Swanton Novers Great Wood, 29 July

- **FLIGHT** Two brooded. Recorded in all months from March–September.
- **DISTRIBUTION** Frequent and widespread.
- **HABITAT** Gardens, grasslands, Brecks, brownfield sites, churchyards, river valleys, woodland rides.
- **FLOWERS VISITED** Dandelion, gorse, hogweed, ragwort, thyme.
- **NESTING** Observed near *Andrena bicolor* nest holes on Kelling Heath and Weybourne. Its distribution in the county is similar to that of *A. bicolor*.

Nomada ferruginata Yellow-shouldered Nomad Bee

♀ [TS]

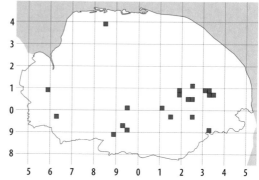

Females: the head and thorax are largely black but the pronotal tubercles are bright yellow and the scutellar tubercles red. The abdomen is red with a round yellow spot on the sides of T2 and sometimes a smaller one on T3. **Males** are similar but have some yellow on the face and there is more yellow on the abdomen, sometimes appearing as yellow bands.

- **FLIGHT** March–May.
- **DISTRIBUTION** Considered rare nationally, but has been relatively frequent in Norfolk since 2010. The distribution approximates to that of its host, *Andrena praecox*.
- **HABITAT** Places with willows and light soils.
- **FLOWERS VISITED** Bluebell, dandelion.
- **NESTING** Known to be a cleptoparasite of *Andrena praecox*, but also observed around a nest aggregation of *A. clarkella* at Strumpshaw Fen (TS).

Nomada flava Flavous Nomad Bee

Females: the antennae and eyes are orange and the face and labrum have orange markings. There are four orange stripes along the thorax and the scutellum is also orange. T1 is orange and black and the remaining tergites are predominantly yellow, with black and orange cross bands. On T2 the yellow band is divided by an orange stripe. **Males** have darker antennae and greenish eyes. The mandibles, labrum and parts of the face are yellow. The tegula and pronotal tubercles are yellow or orange and the scutellar tubercles are orange but the rest of the thorax is black. Males are almost indistinguisable from *Nomada panzeri*.

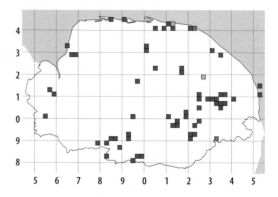

♀, Weybourne, May

♂, Weybourne, 17 May

- **FLIGHT** April–June.
- **DISTRIBUTION** Widespread and common.
- **HABITAT** Gardens, commons, woodland, churchyards, river valleys.
- **FLOWERS VISITED** Cow parsley, dogwood, rhododendron.
- **NESTING** The Norfolk distribution and flight times are similar to that of its main host *Andrena scotica*.

Nomada flavoguttata Little Nomad Bee

♂ on germander speedwell, Felmingham, 15 May

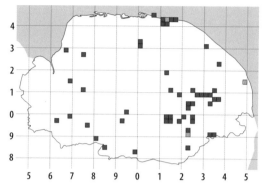

Females: there are orange marks on the face and the labrum is black. The thorax has red lines adjacent to the wings and red scutellar tubercles. There are prominent white hair tufts at each side of the propodeum. The abdomen is red with black cross bands and a small yellow spot at the sides of T2 and T3. **Males** have a black labrum but some yellow on the face. The thorax is entirely black. The abdomen has large yellow marks on the sides of T2–T3 and also a yellow spot on T3.

■ **FLIGHT** March–August.
■ **DISTRIBUTION** Widespread and common.
■ **HABITAT** Commons, woodland, heathland, gardens.
■ **FLOWERS VISITED** Daisy, dandelion, germander speedwell, hogweed.
■ **NESTING** A cleptoparasite of *Andrena minutula* and other *Micrandrena* species.

Nomada flavopicta Blunthorn Nomad Bee

Females: a very striking black and yellow bee. The thorax has prominent yellow tubercles and tegulae and the abdomen has yellow wedges at the sides of T2–T3 with yellow bands on the remaining tergites. The legs are orange and the antennae are dark. **Males** are similar but have yellow on the face and the bands on T1 and T4 are narrowly interrupted.

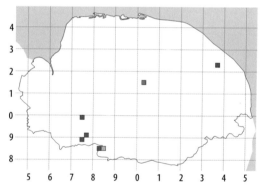

♀, Salisbury Plain, Wiltshire, July

■ **FLIGHT** July–August.
■ **DISTRIBUTION** Most records come from the Brecks including Foulden Common 2009 (TS) and Weeting 2010 (GN). Recorded also from Sutton Fen, 2010 and 2011 and Thetford Warren 2015 (TS). There is a record from North Tuddenham 1948.
■ **HABITAT** Sandy grasslands.
■ **FLOWERS VISITED** Creeping thistle, small scabious, ragwort.
■ **NESTING** Known to be a cleptoparasite of *Melitta* spp. (BWARS). The above records best coincide with *Melitta leporina*.

Nomada fucata Painted Nomad Bee

Females: the eyes are brown, the antennae orange and the thorax is black with prominent yellow markings including the pronotal tubercles, tegulae and scutellar tubercles, which are fused into one bilobed yellow spot. T1 is orange, T2 sometimes partially so and the remaining tergites have yellow bands. **Males** are similar but have green eyes, dark patches on the antennae and some yellow on the face.

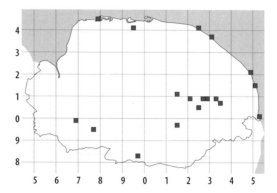

♀ at *Andrena flavipes* nest hole, Stoke Ferry, 16 July

- **FLIGHT** April–September.
- **DISTRIBUTION** First recorded in the county at West Harling in 2006 then at Brancaster Golf Course 2008 (GN). Most records are from 2010 onwards and it is now widespread in the county. However it has so far been recorded at only a small proportion of the sites of its host *Andrena flavipes*.
- **HABITAT** Places with light soils including brownfield sites, cliffs and chalk grassland.
- **FLOWERS VISITED** Fleabane, lavender.
- **NESTING** Observed at *Andrena flavipes* nests at various sites in the county.

♀ on fleabane, Overstrand, 4 August

♂ New Forest, Hampshire, April [PC]

Nomada fulvicornis Orange-horned Nomad Bee

Females: the antennae and facial markings are orange. The thorax is black with prominent yellow markings on the pronotum, protonal tubercles, tegulae and scutellar tubercles, which form two separate yellow spots. There are also paired yellow marks below the tubercles in some individuals. T1–T3 have yellow bands with a black/orange division, broadest in T2. The remaining tergites have yellow bands. **Males** are similar but have yellow facial markings and the scutellar tubercles can be black. There is less orange on the abdomen.

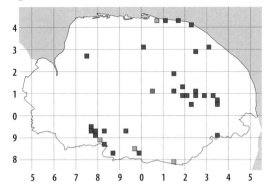

- ■ **FLIGHT** April–July.
- ■ **DISTRIBUTION** Most frequent in the Brecks and around Norwich.
- ■ **HABITAT** Sandy areas including heathland.
- ■ **FLOWERS VISITED** Cinquefoil, dandelion, ragwort, willows.
- ■ **NESTING** Distribution and flight times are consistent with this bee being a cleptoparasite of *Andrena bimaculata*, which has two broods. *A. tibialis* is thought also to be a regular host as it has been seen alongside this species in Brundall almost annually. *A. bimaculata* did not arrive at this site until 2013. *Nomada fulvicornis* associated with *A. tibialis* is thought to be larger (TS).

♀, Hengistbury Head, Dorset, April [PB]

♂, Beeston Common, 1 May

Nomada goodeniana Gooden's Nomad Bee

Females: the antennae and legs are orange and there are yellow and orange markings on the face. The thorax is black with various yellow marks including the widely spaced round yellow scutellar tubercles. The abdomen has yellow bands on a black background without any red markings. T1 is divided by a central black line across the yellow. **Males** are similar but with extensive yellow markings on the face and partially black antennae.

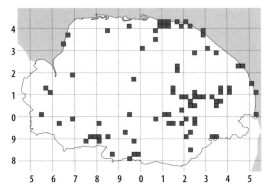

♀, Kelling Heath, 24 May

♂ on forget-me-not, Kelling Heath, 24 May

- ■ **FLIGHT** April–June.
- ■ **DISTRIBUTION** Widespread and common in the county.
- ■ **HABITAT** Varied, including gardens, hedgerows, woodland rides, heathland and scrub.

- ■ **FLOWERS VISITED** Dandelion, forget-me-not, gorse, meadow buttercup, Oxford ragwort,
- ■ **NESTING** The flight times of this *Nomada* coincide with *Andrena nigroaenea*, its known host. Observed at nest holes of *A. nigroaenea* at Beeston Cliffs on 5 May 2011.

Nomada integra Cat's-ear Nomad Bee

Females: the head and thorax are black but the mandibles, tubercles and tegulae are orange. The abdomen is red with some black but no pale markings. The wings have dark edges. **Males** are similar to females with more dark markings on the abdomen.

- ■ **FLIGHT** May–July (BWARS).
- ■ **DISTRIBUTION** There is just one record for this species in the county, from Santon Downham July 1987 (Brecks Project). This was a field observation so is unverified.
- ■ **HABITAT** Breckland grassland.
- ■ **FLOWERS VISITED** No information.
- ■ **NESTING** A cleptoparasite of *Andrena humilis*, which is fairly common in parts of Norfolk. A search of a large *A. humilis* nesting aggregation at Weybourne in May–June 2015 produced no sightings.

Nomada lathburiana Lathbury's Nomad Bee

Females: the antennae are orange and there are orange markings on the face. The thorax is black with reddish hair and yellow pronotal and scutellar tubercles. T1 is rusty-red and black and the remaining tergites have yellow bands with variable amounts of red at the margins and centre line. **Males** are similar but have partially black antennae with sharp points on segments 4–13 and a large amount of yellow on the face. The body hairs are pale.

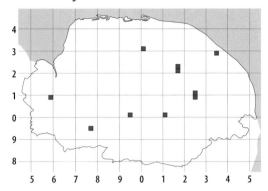

♀, Le Crotoy, France, 13 April

♀, Le Crotoy, France, 22 April

- **FLIGHT** April–June.
- **DISTRIBUTION** A scattering of records across the county, the first being in May 2007 near Watton (GN).

- **HABITAT** Heathland, city parks, cemeteries, woodland rides.
- **FLOWERS VISITED** Gorse.
- **NESTING** Flight times and arrival in the county match those of its host, *Andrena cineraria*.

Nomada leucophthalma Early Nomad Bee

Females: the face and thorax are largely black and the antennae are dark with shining orange tips. The thorax is black with pronotal and scutellar tubercles and tegulae rusty orange. T1 is black and orange, T2 and T3 are yellow divided by orange and the remaining tergites have yellow bands.
Males The antennae are very dark and there is a small yellow triangle on the face adjacent to the yellow mandibles. The entire thorax is black including the tegulae and the abdomen is similar to females but darker.

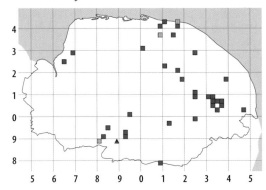

- ■ **FLIGHT** March–May.
- ■ **DISTRIBUTION** Distribution and flight times closely reflect those of its host *Andrena clarkella*.
- ■ **HABITAT** Woodland, scrub, heathland and parkland. Some large *A. clarkella* nesting aggregations are under the tree canopy in woodlands and city parks, but get some sunlight because the nesting season is very early.
- ■ **FLOWERS VISITED** Willows.
- ■ **NESTING** Observed at nesting aggregations of *A. clarkella* on root plates, bare ground at the base of trees and banks/bare ground on heathland.

♀, Kelling Heath, 9 May

♀, Kelling Heath, 30 March

♂, Rewell Wood, West Sussex [PB]

Nomada marshamella Marsham's Nomad Bee

Females: the antennae are orange and there are orange marks on the lower face and beside each eye. There are yellow marks on the pronotum behind the head and the pronotal and scutellar tubercles are also yellow. The tegulae are orange, helping to distinguish this species from *Nomada goodeniana*. The abdomen is black with yellow bands, the bands being divided centrally in T1–T3. In T1 the yellow areas can be quite small. **Males** have yellow markings on the face and orange tegulae (sometimes partly yellow). The yellow marks on the thorax are reduced in size and the scutellum can be entirely black.

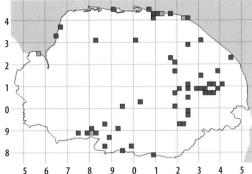

- **FLIGHT** Mid April–June: a rather short flight period.
- **DISTRIBUTION** Widespread in the county.
- **HABITAT** Woodlands, gardens, commons, heathland, hedgerows.
- **FLOWERS VISITED** Dandelion, hogweed.
- **NESTING** The distribution and flight times correspond with its known host *Andrena scotica* and are also similar to *Nomada flava* which shares this host.

♀, Beeston Common, 24 May

♀, Weybourne, 15 May

♂ [TB]

Nomada obtusifrons Flat-ridged Nomad Bee

Females: both sexes have a flat ridge between the antennae, which are dark. The face and thorax are black with a small yellow mark on the pronotal tubercles. The abdomen is red with large yellow marks on the sides of T2–T3 with further yellow and black markings on T4–T6. **Males** have a divided yellow mark on the clypeus and yellow mandibles.

- **FLIGHT** July–August.
- **DISTRIBUTION** Recorded at Brundall in the 19th century by Bridgman and by Wainright at West Runton in 1900. It could still be present in Norfolk.
- **HABITAT** Lane near West Runton and a field at Brundall.
- **FLOWERS VISITED** Creeping thistle.
- **NESTING** A cleptoparasite of *Andrena coitana*.

♀, Cornwall, 20 July [PS]

Nomada panzeri Panzer's Nomad Bee

Females: this species is very difficult to separate from *Nomada flava*. *N. panzeri* females can be very dark, with the orange markings on the thorax less contrasting with their background. The hairs on the face are dark rather than yellow but the hairs on the sides of the thorax are whiter than in *N. flava*. There is usually more red on the tergites (but not usually so extensive as in *N. ruficornis*). **Males** have yellow markings on the face and yellow pronotal tubercles. The antennae are blackened only at the base: entirely blackened in *N. flava* males (SF).

- **FLIGHT** April–June.
- **DISTRIBUTION** Widely distributed but with fewer records in the west.
- **HABITAT** Woodland rides, hedgerows, scrub, cliffs.
- **FLOWERS VISITED** Germander speedwell, hogweed, thrift, thyme.

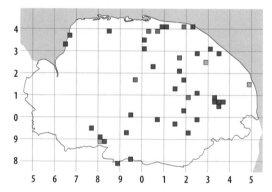

- **NESTING** A cleptoparasite of several closely related *Andrena* species, including *A. fulva* and *A. synadelpha*. The Norfolk distribution best fits *A. synadelpha*.

♀ [TB]

♂ on thrift, Weybourne, 10 May

Nomada roberjeotiana Tormentil Nomad Bee

Females have orange mandibles, labrum and tip to the clypeus. The antennae are orange with a dark upper surface. The legs are largely orange. The thorax is black with orange pronotal tubercles and tegulae. The scutellar tubercles are fused orange. The abdomen is orange anteriorly grading to black with wedge shaped cream marks at the sides from T2–T3 and a yellow mark on T5. **Males** The face is largely yellow and there is a yellow collar on the thorax. The pronotal tubercles and tegulae are also yellow. Other markings resemble those of females.

♀ on tormentil, Cornwall, 29 July [PS]

- **FLIGHT** July–August.
- **DISTRIBUTION** Atmore 1909 writes "King's Lynn. Usually considered a rare species but I have taken a long series in July and August at the flowers of Common Ragwort". These are the only county records.

- **HABITAT** As for *Andrena tarsata*: sites rich in tormentil.
- **FLOWERS VISITED** Ragwort and tormentil.
- **NESTING** A cleptoparasite of *Andrena tarsata*.

Nomada ruficornis Fork-jawed Nomad Bee

Females: this is one of three very similar species, the others being *Nomada flava* and *N. panzeri*. This is the only one of the three with two teeth at the tips of the mandibles. In *N. ruficornis* the eyes are a rich chestnut colour (paler brown in the other two species) and the red markings on the top of the head are more extensive, almost surrounding the ocelli. The hairs on the thorax are more upright and longer and there is normally more red and less yellow on the abdomen, but the extent varies and overlaps with the other two species. **Males** also have bifid mandibles but are otherwise very difficult to distinguish from the two similar species.

♀ on hogweed, Weybourne, 21 June

♀, Weybourne, 14 May

- **FLIGHT** April–June.
- **DISTRIBUTION** Widespread across the county.
- **HABITAT** Very varied: woods, hedgerows, gardens, heathland, parkland, scrub, churchyards.

- **FLOWERS VISITED** Germander speedwell, hogweed.
- **NESTING** Flight times and distribution correspond to its host, *Andrena haemorrhoa*.

Nomada rufipes Black-horned Nomad Bee

Females: the antennae are dark and there are red markings on the face. The thorax is black with yellow markings. The fused yellow spots of the scutellar tubercles make identification easy, as they are otherwise seen only in *Nomada fucata*, which has bright orange antennae. The abdomen is tricoloured in some individuals but in others the abdomen has no red at all. **Males** resemble the black form of the female and have more yellow on the face.

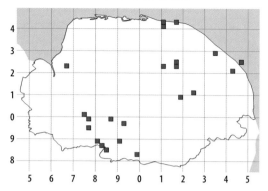

♀ red form, Stanta, 19 September

♀ black form, Kelling Heath, 13 August

♂, Kelling Heath, 14 August

- **FLIGHT** Late June–September.
- **DISTRIBUTION** Recorded at most heathland sites in the county.
- **HABITAT** Largely recorded on heathland with heather, the habitat of its main host, *Andrena fuscipes*.
- **FLOWERS VISITED** Canadian goldenrod, heather (ling).
- **NESTING** Usually seen near nest sites of *Andrena fuscipes*, but also recorded at Weybourne Camp and Hickling Broad, where there is no heather, and at Beeston Common where there is some heather but *A. fuscipes* seems to be absent. *A. denticulata*, another known host of *Nomada rufipes*, has been recorded at these three sites and is the probable host

Nomada sexfasciata Six-banded Nomad Bee

Last recorded in Norfolk at Postwick in the 19th century by Bridgman when it was numerous at a nesting aggregation of *Eucera longicornis*. There are no Norfolk records of either species since the 1870s.

♀, Prawle Point, Devon [SF]

Nomada sheppardana Sheppard's Nomad Bee

This is the smallest of our Nomad Bees. Both sexes are very dark. **Females** have dark antennae with yellow tips. The thorax is black with red tegulae and red protonal and scutellar tubercles. The abdomen is also black with red bands on T1 and T2. **Males** have yellow on the face and a largely dark thorax. The abdomen has indistinct red bands and various spots and flecks of yellow.

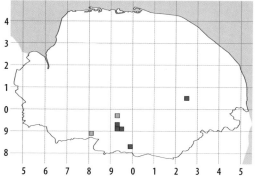

♀, Rewell Wood, West Sussex [PB]

- **FLIGHT** May–August.
- **DISTRIBUTION** Recorded in the Brecks and at Caister Quarry (TS).
- **HABITAT** Places with chalky sand including Caister Quarry (TS) and a sand pit at Hockham Woods (GN).
- **FLOWERS VISITED** No information.
- **NESTING** The Norfolk distribution does not match any of its known *Lasioglossum* hosts. It is possible that it requires a subset of the host's habitats, perhaps those which are hottest.

Nomada signata Broad-banded Nomad Bee

Females: there are orange marks on the head and four orange lines along the top of the thorax. The tegulae and scutellar tubercles are also red. These features are shared by *Nomada flava*, *N. panzeri* and *N. ruficornis* but *N. signata* can be distinguished from these three species by the large yellow marks on its propodeum. Also, the yellow bands on the abdomen are deeper with narrower dark dividing bands. **Males** are more difficult to separate but also have deep yellow bands on the abdomen with straight front and back edges. T1 often has larger yellow spots than in males of similar species.

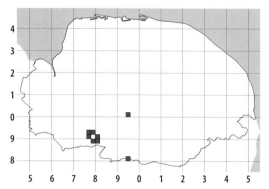

Possible ♂, Walsey Hills [JF]

- **FLIGHT** April–May.
- **DISTRIBUTION** There is cluster of recent records in the Cranwich/Weeting/Santon Downham area, all 2010 or later. Isolated records come from east of Thetford on the Suffolk border (2001), near Watton (2010–11) with a possible record at Walsey Hills near Cley (JF 2014). There are two pre-2000 records: Santon Downham 1986 and near Norwich 1942. These records suggest a recent increase in this scarce species.
- **HABITAT** Sandy or gravelly grassland with some gorse and scrub.
- **FLOWERS VISITED** No information.
- **NESTING** Known to be a cleptoparasite of *Andrena fulva*, but absent from much of this host's range in the county.

Nomada striata Blunt-jawed Nomad Bee

Females: the antennae are orange and there are orange marks on the head. There are orange stripes on the top of the thorax and the tubercles and tegulae are also orange. The abdomen is largely orange and black but has large yellow spots of T2, small ones on T3 and yellow bars on T4 and T5. **Males** are similar but have some yellow on the face and lack stripes on the thorax.

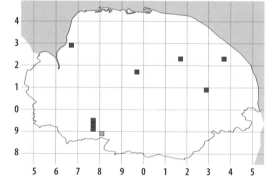

♀, Sutton Fen, 17 June [TS]

- **FLIGHT** May–July.
- **DISTRIBUTION** A scattering of records across the county, but rather scarce. Recorded at Norwich by Bridgman in the 19th century.
- **HABITAT** Grasslands and heathland with Fabaceae.
- **FLOWERS VISITED** Gorse.
- **NESTING** Known to be a cleptoparasite of *Andrena wilkella*, but no direct evidence from Norfolk.

This genus of smallish dumpy bees comprises two quite similar British species, both occurring in Norfolk. They are cleptoparasites of various *Colletes* species and can often be seen at their nesting aggregations, crouched on the ground or entering nest holes. The eyes are reddish brown and the black body bears various paired white bars and spots composed of flattened short white hairs. The legs are red and black and the tongue is moderately long.

Epeolus cruciger Red-thighed Epeolus

Females have a black face with red labrum and mandibles. There are orange markings on the anterior edge of the thorax with a white area beneath each wing. The protonal tubercles, tegulae and scutellar tubercles are red. The abdomen has paired bars or spots on each tergite. The legs are almost entirely red (partly black in *Epeolus variegatus*) and the abdomen is less protruding than in that species. **Males** have a black face with red mandibles and partially red labrum. The tegulae are orange but there are no other orange marks on the thorax. The femora are partly black and the pygidium is partially red (black in *E. variegatus*).

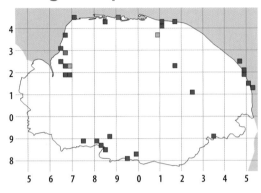

- **FLIGHT** July–September.
- **DISTRIBUTION** Found mostly where there is heather (ling), reflecting the distribution of its main host, *Colletes succinctus*.
- **HABITAT** Heathland with heather and other sandy areas.
- **FLOWERS VISITED** Hawkweed, heather (ling), ragwort, field scabious.
- **NESTING** A parasite of *Colletes succinctus*. *C. marginatus* is another known host (BWARS) and may be targeted where it occurs (mostly in the Brecks). This *Epeolus* may be genetically distinct (SF).

♀, Weybourne Cliffs, 19 August

♀ on heather, Kelling Heath, 28 August

♀ apparently laying eggs, presumably into a nest of *Colletes succinctus* beneath the sand, Kelling Heath, 13 August

Epeolus variegatus Black-thighed Epeolus

Females differ from *Epeolus cruciger* in having dark markings on some parts of the legs, including the mid and hind femora. The tip of the abdomen is more pointed. **Males**: the pygidium is usually black but it requires microscopic details of genitalia to confirm identity.

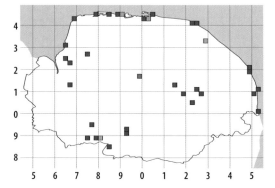

♀ on fleabane, Weybourne Camp, 13 August

- **FLIGHT** July–August.
- **DISTRIBUTION** Recorded on the north and east coast, west Norfolk, the Brecks and the Norwich area.
- **HABITAT** Coastal marshes, cliffs and dunes, chalk grassland, and areas of light soils including the Brecks.
- **FLOWERS VISITED** Fleabane, ragwort, tansy.
- **NESTING** Associated with nesting aggregations of *Colletes halophilus* e.g. at Breydon Water August 2011 (TS). Records from the north and south-east corner of the county indicate this host, which is associated with saltmarshes. Elsewhere possible hosts include *C. daviesanus* and *C. fodiens* (BWARS).

These are large and conspicuous bees with some resemblance to *Anthophora* or *Bombus*. They collect pollen on their hind legs and sometimes nest in aggregations. The forewings have two sub-marginal cells (three in *Anthophora* and *Bombus*). There are two British species with one recorded in Norfolk in the 19th century, but thought now to be extinct in the county.

Eucera longicornis Long-horned Bee

Females are large and broad with pale hair on most body areas and reddish-brown hair on the thorax. The pollen hairs on the hind legs are long and pale and there are also long pale hairs on the sides of the tergites. **Males** have a similar colour pattern and are instantly recogniseble by the extreme length of their antennae

- **FLIGHT** May–June.
- **DISTRIBUTION** Presumed extinct. Bridgman 1879 writes "Not uncommon round Norwich. There is also a large colony extending about a quarter of a mile by the roadside at Postwick; they make their appearance about the end of May". These are the only reports of the species in the county but it probably survived into the 20th century.
- **HABITAT** Grasslands rich in Fabaceae (BWARS).
- **FLOWERS VISITED** Often use Fabaceae (BWARS).
- **NESTING** Nests in the ground in aggregations (see above).
- **PARASITES** *Nomada sexfasciata*: recorded on the Postwick site by Bridgman in the 1870s.

♀ on vetch sp., Cornwall, 15 June [PS]

♂ on daisy, Cornwall, 23 May [PS]

These are large bees with a very active darting fight, often hovering, with a round shape and a long tongue. Flowers with a deep corolla are often used as a nectar source and pollen is collected on the hind tibiae. The forewings have three submarginal cells and the hair is long, giving a resemblance to a small bumblebee. The males of some species have distinctive hairs on their legs. There are white or yellow markings on the face in one or both sexes, and there is considerable sexual dimorphism. Large nesting aggregations can occur in soft cliffs or mortar, though some species nest in stems or wood. They are parasitised by bees in the genera *Melecta* and *Coelioxys*. There are five British species, all recorded in Norfolk, but one now extinct.

Anthophora quadrimaculata ♀, on viper's-bugloss, Cambridge Botanic Garden, 15 June

Anthophora plumipes pair, Oxford, April [PC]

Anthophora bimaculata Green-eyed Flower Bee

Females: this is the only British *Anthophora* in which the female as well as the male has yellow facial markings. These form a band at the base of the clypeus with a narrow upward extension, and the mandibles are also yellow. The eyes are large and pale green and the tongue is fairly long. The thorax has a mixture of brown and black hairs with paler hairs under the wings. There are long white pollen hairs on the hind tibia and white bands on the tergites. It is the smallest British member of the genus. **Males** resemble females but have more extensive pale markings on the face. The scape is also pale beneath.

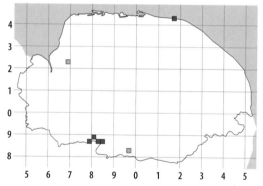

♀ (worn), Essex [TB]

- **FLIGHT** July–August.
- **DISTRIBUTION** Recorded in the Brecks in the Santon Downham area. Isolated records come from Roydon Common 1996 (MA), Sheringham 2001 (KD) and West Harling 1991 (KD).
- **HABITAT** Brecks grassland, heathland and commons.
- **FLOWERS VISITED** No Norfolk information. Polylectic (BWARS).
- **NESTING** No Norfolk information. Often nests on sloping exposed earth in aggregations (BWARS).
- **PARASITES** *Coelioxys rufescens* and possibly other *Coelioxys* spp. (BWARS).

Anthophora furcata Fork-tailed Flower Bee

Females have a covering of ginger-brown hair with similar coloured tibia hairs. There are black hairs on the top of the head and a mix of black and brown on the upper thorax. The hair on the face and the tip of the abdomen is reddish. The abdomen has long hair but no clear hair bands. The eyes are dark. **Males** have similar hair colour to females. The face and labrum have a large pale yellow area. There is a forked extension at the tip of the abdomen. The abdomen can look banded when worn.

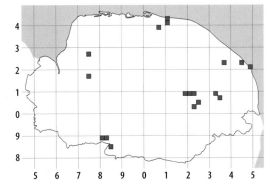

- **FLIGHT** Late May–early October.
- **DISTRIBUTION** Widespread with records mostly around Norwich, the Brecks and the Kelling Heath area.
- **HABITAT** Associated with light soils, including coastal sites, heathland, Breckland and chalk grassland. Sometimes attracted to sweaty skin.

- **FLOWERS VISITED** False dittany, black horehound, foxglove, lavender, marsh woundwort, sage, spear thistle, white dead-nettle.
- **NESTING** No Norfolk information. Excavates holes in rotting wood (BWARS). It will also occupy stems in 'bee hotels'.
- **PARASITES** *Coelioxys quadridentata* and *C. rufescens* (BWARS).

♀ on spear thistle, Weybourne, 31 July

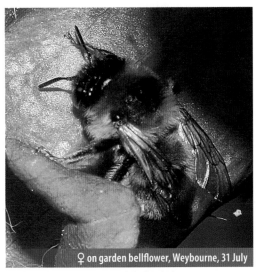

♀ on garden bellflower, Weybourne, 31 July

Anthophora plumipes Hairy-footed Flower Bee

Females have black hair except for the hind tibia and tarsus which have orange pollen collecting hairs. The tongue is very long in both sexes.
Males are largely ginger-brown and are often mistaken for carder bumblebees. They have a large area of pale yellow on the long face and a pale yellow marking beneath the antennal scape. They have long hairs on the mid tibia, giving the species its common name.

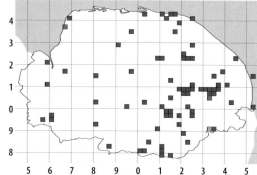

- **FLIGHT** March–early June.
- **DISTRIBUTION** Abundant and widespread.
- **HABITAT** Gardens, hedge banks, churchyards, commons, river valleys, cliffs, dunes, woodland rides.
- **FLOWERS VISITED** Bluebell, broccoli, comfrey, flowering currant, red dead-nettle, white dead-nettle, gorse, grape hyacinth, ground-ivy, garden heather, hellebore, lungwort, garden plum, cherry plum, primrose, rosemary.
- **NESTING** Nests in aggregations, sometimes in thousands, in the walls of buildings and on cliffs.
- **PARASITES** *Melecta albifrons* is a common cleptoparasite.

♀ on daphne, Weybourne, 22 March

♂ on red dead-nettle, Weybourne, 23 March

♂ with tongue extended, Oxford, April [PC]

Anthophora quadrimaculata Four-banded Flower Bee

Females have brown hair with pale bands on the tergites, narrower than in *Anthophora bimaculata*. There are no pale markings on the face. The eyes are greenish in both sexes. **Males** are similar, with a covering of hair on T1 and bands of long hair on the remaining tergites. The face has a large pale area broken by a pair of dark triangular markings.

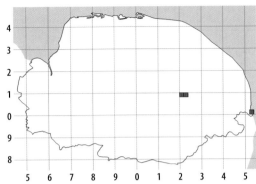

♀ on catmint, Cambridge Botanic Garden, 15 June

♂, Cambridge Botanic Garden, 25 June

- **FLIGHT** June–September.
- **DISTRIBUTION** Recorded in a west Norwich garden September 1982 (AI) with further records from a nearby garden in 2013-16 with up to three present between 14 June and 30 August (JB). Also recorded in a Norwich garden, 20 July 2010 and on Gorleston Cliff, July 2015 (both TS).
- **HABITAT** Gardens, soft cliffs.

- **FLOWERS VISITED** Recorded on the following in west Norwich 2013-16 (JB): false dittany, catmint, ivy-leaved toadflax, lavender, *Linaria* sp., garden lobelia, red valerian.
- **NESTING** Observed entering a hole on the cliff face at Gorleston loaded with yellow pollen (TS). Known to nest in small aggregations (BWARS).
- **PARASITES** None reported (BWARS).

Anthophora retusa Potter Flower Bee

This species closely resembles *Anthophora plumipes* but is smaller and slimmer (SF). **Females** have black hair and orange tibia spurs rather than black. **Males** are brown and lack very long hairs on the legs. The pale markings on the face are less extensive than in *A. plumipes*.

- **FLIGHT** April–June (BWARS).
- **DISTRIBUTION** Paget 1834 records it as "very common in gardens" in the Yarmouth area. Bridgman 1879 describes it as 'plentiful at Mousehold and neighbourhood' with most appearing in May. There are no further county records and the species is now very rare nationally.
- **HABITAT** Sandy soils including the coast (BWARS).
- **FLOWERS VISITED** Polylectic (BWARS).
- **NESTING** Nest in the ground (BWARS).
- **PARASITES** *Melecta luctuosa* which may be extinct in the British Isles (BWARS).

There is just one member of this genus in Norfolk and two nationally, the second one probably extinct. They are cleptoparasites, attacking the nests of *Anthophora* species and do not collect their own pollen. The body has long brown, black and white hairs, giving the bee a spotted appearance. There are three submarginal cells on the forewing and the tongue is long. They are most easily found at nest sites of their host but also visit flowers, sometimes in gardens.

Melecta albifrons Common Mourning Bee

Females have black hairs on the clypeus and behind the eyes and pale brown hairs on the upper head and thorax (some black hairs intermixed) with whitish hair under the wings. The tergites have a row of white spots along each side, decreasing in size. The tips of the antennae are slanted in both sexes. There is a white hair patch at the centre of the mid and hind tibiae in both sexes. **Males** are very similar to females.

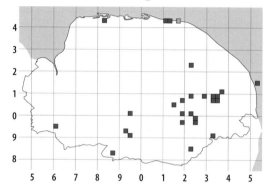

- **FLIGHT** March–May.
- **DISTRIBUTION** Widespread in the east of the county but seemingly scarce in the west. Twenty or more were observed basking on the cliff edge at Weybourne above a large nesting aggregation in the cliff face numbering 1,000+.
- **HABITAT** As for *Anthophora plumipes*.
- **FLOWERS VISITED** Comfrey, red dead-nettle.
- **NESTING** A cleptoparasite of *A. plumipes*. Probably present at all large nesting aggregations.

♀ at *Anthophora plumipes* nest hole, Weybourne, 27 April

♂ at *Anthophora plumipes* nest hole, Weybourne, 2 April

♀ on red dead-nettle with orange pollen on its head, Weybourne, 24 March

Large hairy bees which are mostly eusocial, having queens, workers and males. There is a pollen basket on the hind tibia, otherwise present only in Honeybees.

Queens emerge from hibernation in the first warm days of spring. Nests are established underground (often in an empty mouse nest hole), near the surface amongst leaf litter (carder bumblebees) or in a cavity in a tree or building (especially *Bombus hypnorum*). Workers soon emerge and take over the role of bringing pollen and nectar to the brood. Later in the season new queens and males are produced. Mating occurs followed by hibernation by the queen. All males and workers die off.

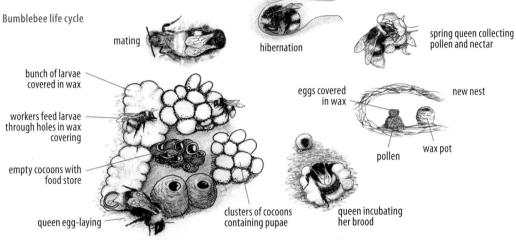

Bumblebee life cycle

mating

hibernation

spring queen collecting pollen and nectar

bunch of larvae covered in wax

eggs covered in wax

new nest

workers feed larvae through holes in wax covering

empty cocoons with food store

queen egg-laying

clusters of cocoons containing pupae

queen incubating her brood

pollen

wax pot

Bombus hypnorum queen showing the triangular pollen basket fringed by hairs on the hind tibia

Bombus vestalis ♀ cuckoo bumblebee showing the hair-covered hind tibia and dark wings

Sixteen true bumblebee species have been recorded in Norfolk (out of 19 in the British Isles) of which one is a vagrant and four appear to be extinct in the county. In addition all six British species of cuckoo bumblebee occur in Norfolk. These are described after the true bumblebees. A cuckoo bumblebee female enters the nest of its host and overpowers the queen, then lays its own eggs, which are tended by the host workers. There are no worker cuckoos, only females and males. Cuckoo bumblebees can be recognised by their sluggish movements on flowers and soft buzz. They lack a pollen basket and have a strong cuticle with a robust sting. The wings have a brownish tint. Cuckoo bumblebees can be abundant, even out-numbering their host locally at times. Females are seen less than males because they go into hibernation soon after hatching and mating.

Hind leg of bumblebee (left) and cuckoo bumblebee (right)

pollen basket (corbicula)

tibia

convex hair-covered tibia – no pollen basket

comb

pollen press

basitarsus

Bombus distinguendus Great Yellow Bumblebee

Queen on meadow vetchling, Lewis, Outer Hebrides, July

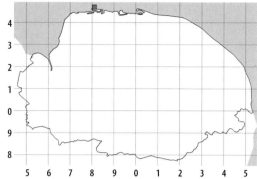

Queens, workers and males share a similar colour pattern, being entirely yellow haired except for a black band between the wings. The tongue is fairly long.

- **FLIGHT** May–September.
- **DISTRIBUTION** This is a northern species which was probably never abundant in Norfolk. The first county record (as *Bombus fragrans*) comes from Paget 1834 as being "rather rare" around Yarmouth. Bridgman recorded a nest at Brundall in the 1870s as well as finding specimens at Mousehold, Yarmouth and Cromer. He described it as "far from common". It is on a list of insects of Scolt Head Island published in 1960 but the date of the actual observation is not given (EAE). Plowright did not find any in the county in the 1960s.
- **HABITAT** Flower rich grasslands, especially near the coast.
- **FLOWERS VISITED** Especially clovers and other Fabaceae.
- **NESTING** In small mammal burrows amongst long grass, but sometimes deeper down. Bridgman describes a nest at Brundall "In the middle of August I found a nest of *Bombus fragrans* (which generally builds on the ground) on a bank, and though I dug about 18 inches to two feet, I could not reach it."
- **PARASITES** None reported in the British Isles.

♂ on marsh woundwort, Orkney, 28 August

Worker on red clover, Caithness, August

Bombus hortorum Garden Bumblebee

Queens, **workers** and **males** have a similar colour pattern with a yellow band on the collar, the scutellum and the first two abdominal segments. The tail is white. Males can have yellow hairs on the top of the head and are sometimes darkened in colour. The head is very long, housing a very long tongue.

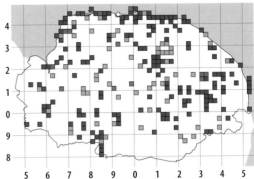

Queen on kidney vetch, Weybourne, 9 June

- **FLIGHT** Queens generally emerge in the first half of April but many are still active outside the nest in May or even June. The season ends around September.
- **DISTRIBUTION** This is a common bumblebee with records spread fairly evenly across the county.
- **HABITAT** Gardens, waysides, parkland, woodland rides.
- **FLOWERS VISITED** Able to access flowers with a deep corolla such as red clover, honeysuckle dead-nettles, sages, garden delphinium, large bindweed and primrose, but will also use unspecialised flowers.
- **NESTING** Uses holes in the ground including those made by small mammals but will also nest in decaying plant debris.
- **PARASITES** *Bombus barbutellus*.

Worker on garden sage, Weybourne, August

♂, Warham Camp, 3 September

Bombus humilis Brown-banded Carder Bumblebee

Queens, **workers** and **males** are similar. This species resembles *Bombus muscorum* in lacking black hairs, though *B. humilis* can have a few at the wing bases. There is a brownish band on T2 giving the species its name, but certain identification is not always possible in the field or from images. The tongue is quite long.

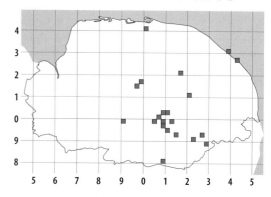

Worker on red clover, Castlemartin, Pembrokeshire, 10 July

♂ on a labiate, Beaune, France, 11 September

- **FLIGHT** May–September (BWARS).
- **DISTRIBUTION** This species has a southerly distribution in the British Isles with Norfolk being about its most northerly (former) limit. It is described as "not uncommon" by Bridgman 1879. Durrant collected specimens from four county localities in the 1950s and it was last recorded by Plowright in the 1960s from east and south Norfolk. It is now thought to be extinct in the county. It was rediscovered (or had recolonised) Suffolk in 2005/6.

- **HABITAT** Dependent on permanent grasslands rich in flowers, a habitat which has greatly declined in Norfolk. Its last stronghold was the claylands to the south west of Norwich. It possibly survives un-noticed.
- **FLOWERS VISITED** A wide variety including those with a moderately deep corolla such as clovers.
- **NESTING** Amongst grass made of carded vegetation.
- **PARASITES** Possibly *Bombus campestris* (BWARS).

Bombus hypnorum Tree Bumblebee

Queens and **workers**: the hair on the thorax is bright gingery brown, though sometimes this is darkened. The abdomen is black with a contrasting white tail. The tongue is fairly short. **Males** usually have ginger-brown hair on T1–T2.

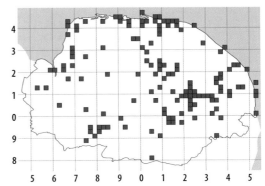

- ■ **FLIGHT** April–August.
- ■ **DISTRIBUTION** This species is extending its range in mainland Europe and was first seen in southern England in 2001. It was first recorded in Norfolk in Earlham Cemetery in 2008 (SP). In 2009 it was established across a wide area of the county up to the north coast, and it is now one of the most abundant bumblebees in the county.
- ■ **HABITAT** Gardens, hedgerows, woodland edge, scrub.
- ■ **FLOWERS VISITED** A wide range of species, but the short tongue prevents access to flowers with a deep corolla. Records include bramble, hawthorn, rosebay willowherb and rowan.
- ■ **NESTING** Nests are usually above the ground, in tree holes, bird nest boxes or buildings, often under roof tiles. Nest activity generally ends in June but there is sometimes a second brood. Queens have been found hibernating in rotting logs (TH).
- ■ **PARASITES** None confirmed.

Queen on greater burdock, Cambridge, 1 August

♂ on bramble, Kelling Heath, 8 June

Queen, dark form on willow, Beeston Common, April

Bombus jonellus Heath Bumblebee

Queens and **workers** resemble a small *Bombus hortorum*, having three yellow bands and a white tail. However, the face is much rounder and the tongue is short. The hairs on the pollen basket are usually reddish in colour. Queens and workers are sometimes very dark with greatly reduced yellow bands. **Males** have yellow on the face and the thorax is largely yellow except for a black band between the wings. The abdomen is yellow anteriorly and the tail is white.

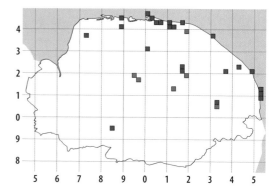

- ■ **FLIGHT** March–September.
- ■ **DISTRIBUTION** Most recent records come from the coast with a scatter of inland sightings. Numbers seem to fluctuate from year to year. There are pre-1980 records mostly from the centre of the county.
- ■ **HABITAT** Long established habitats including heathland, dunes, vegetated shingle, mature gardens, Peddars Way and Stanta, Brecks.
- ■ **FLOWERS VISITED** Willows, ground-ivy, flowering currant, bell heather, heather, cotoneaster.
- ■ **NESTING** In sandy ground and also recorded in in a bird nesting box in oak scrub. There are two broods per year.
- ■ **PARASITES** Probably *Bombus sylvestris*.

Queen, Kelling Heath, 26 August

♂ on bell heather, Braemar, Aberdeenshire,14 September

Worker on heather, Kelling Heath, 27 August

Bombus lapidarius Red-tailed Bumblebee

Queens and **workers** are all black with a red tail. The **male** has a yellow collar extending round the underside, and yellow hairs on the face. There are often some yellow hairs or a yellow band at the back of the thorax, and sometimes on T1. The tongue is short.

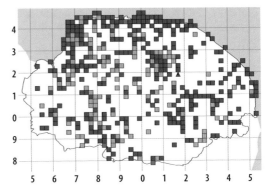

Queen on thrift, Weybourne, 9 June

Worker on bird's-foot-trefoil, Weybourne, 9 June

♂ on black knapweed, Swanton Novers Great Wood, 11 September

Mating pair, Kelling Heath, 21 July

- **FLIGHT** April–October.
- **DISTRIBUTION** Common and widespread with a concentration along the north coast.
- **HABITAT** Gardens, coastal grazing marshes, vegetated shingle, heathland, hedgerows, grasslands, woodland rides.

- **FLOWERS VISITED** A very wide range but not those with a deep corolla. The workers can be nimble and small and are able to access small flowers such as yellow clovers.
- **NESTING** Holes of small mammals or cavities under stones or roots.
- **PARASITES** *Bombus rupestris*.

Bombus lucorum White-tailed Bumblebee

Queens and **workers** have two bright yellow bands and a pure white tail. **Males** are variable, but always have a lot of yellow hair, especially on the face, top of the head, scutellum and T1. Two closely related species/races *Bombus cryptarum* and *B. magnus*, are widespread in Scotland and occur locally in other parts of the British Isles. Separating these three taxa reliably requires DNA analysis.

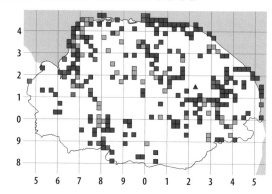

- ■ **FLIGHT** March–October.
- ■ **DISTRIBUTION** One of the commonest bumblebees, found throughout the county, perhaps under-recorded through confusion with *Bombus terrestris*.
- ■ **HABITAT** Gardens, farmland, woodland edge, heathland and coastal areas.
- ■ **FLOWERS VISITED** The tongue is fairly short, restricting this species to flowers with a short corolla. They can, however, use their mandibles to make holes in long-corolla flowers, allowing them to nectar-rob species such as red campion, comfrey, bell heather and fuschia. They often frequent bramble and hogweed flowers and can be common on bell heather.
- ■ **NESTING** Generally uses nest holes of small mammals, sometimes in lawns.
- ■ **PARASITES** *Bombus bohemicus*.

Queen on gorse, Swanton Novers Great Wood, 16 May

♂ on black knapweed, Swanton Novers Great Wood, 11 September

Worker on hogweed, Weybourne, 11 June

Bombus monticola Bilberry Bumblebee

Queens and **workers**: the collar is pale yellow, and there is a second yellow band at the back of the thorax. T3–T6 have red hair, this red being more extensive than in *Bombus lapidarius*.
Males are similar to queens and workers but with much more yellow hair, including a large patch on the face and the top of the head.

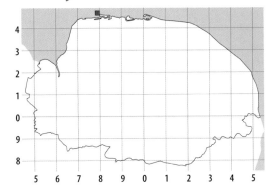

- **FLIGHT** April–October.
- **DISTRIBUTION** This species is largely confined to upland moors and their fringes in the north and west of Britain. It was added to the Norfolk list in 2007, when three males, presumed vagrants, were recorded on Scolt Head NNR.
- **HABITAT** Moorland, usually with bilberries.
- **FLOWERS VISITED** No Norfolk information: bell heather, bilberry, dandelion, heather, rosebay willowherb in other regions.
- **NESTING** Underground often in old mammal nest holes (BWARS).
- **PARASITES** *Bombus sylvestris* (BWARS).

Queen, Newtonmore, Inverness-shire, September

♂ on rosebay willowherb, Eyam Moor, Derbyshire, 8 August

Worker on ragwort, Glenshee, Aberdeenshire, 15 September

Bombus muscorum Moss Carder Bumblebee

Queens, **workers** and **males** are similar. Unlike *Bombus pascuorum* there are no black hairs on the thorax or abdomen. When fresh, the thorax is a bright orange-ginger with paler almost lemon-yellow edges and also paler hairs at the front and back of the thorax. The hair on the thorax is even and short. There can be an indistinct brownish band on segment two of the abdomen, causing possible confusion with *B. humilis*. The tongue is quite long. Males of the three brown carder species can be separated by examining the genitalia.

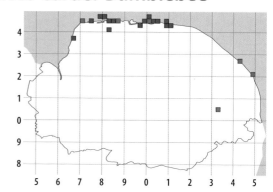

Queen, Burnham Overy, May [JF]

- ■ **FLIGHT** May–August.
- ■ **DISTRIBUTION** Described as "common" in 1834 around Yarmouth by Paget. Bridgman 1879 describes it as "very abundant" around Norwich [but there is a possibility of confusion with *Bombus pascuorum* owing to nomenclature change]. Recent records all come from a band along the north coast. It is scarce and possibly declining.
- ■ **HABITAT** Coastal marshes, grasslands, dunes and dyke sides with abundant flowers in late spring.
- ■ **FLOWERS VISITED** Lamiaceae, Fabaceae, knapweeds, field scabious.
- ■ **NESTING** A carder species, nesting amongst grass above ground (BWARS).
- ■ **PARASITES** Possibly *Bombus campestris*.

Worker on field scabious, Weybourne, 8 August

♂ on field scabious, Weybourne, 8 August

Bombus pascuorum Common Carder Bumblebee

Queens and **workers**: the head is long, as is the tongue. The thorax is ginger brown, fading to pale sandy brown in older specimens. The abdomen is also ginger-brown with variable amounts of black hair, making the abdomen look stripy in some individuals. **Males** can be distinguished by their longer antennae. Some individuals can have virtually no black hair and resemble other brown carder species.

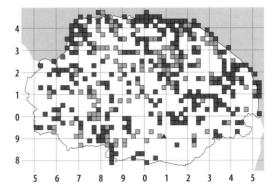

- **FLIGHT** March–November. Can be active in poor weather.
- **DISTRIBUTION** One of the commonest and most widespread bumblebees in Norfolk with a strong population along the north coast.
- **HABITAT** Gardens, hedgerows, verges, woodland edge.
- **FLOWERS VISITED** Especially members of the Lamiaceae, Fabaceae, Orobanchaceae, Scrophulariaceae and Veronicaceae. Also visits spring blossom including blackthorn and apple.
- **NESTING** Nests above ground among moss and other leaf litter, which is carded into a loose ball.
- **PARASITES** *Bombus campestris*.

Queen on yellow archangel,
Swanton Novers Great Wood, 5 May

♂ on devil's-bit scabious,
Swanton Novers Great Wood, 11 September

Worker on meadow vetchling, Beeston Common, 16 June

Bombus pratorum Early Bumblebee

Queens and **workers** are small with a red tail and yellow collar. There is usually a yellow band on T2 but this can be reduced or absent. **Males** have a broad yellow collar extending round the underside. There is a lot of yellow hair on the head and face. T1-2 are also yellow. The tongue is short and narrow.

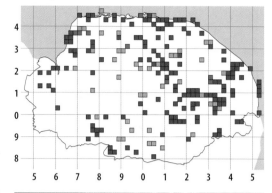

Queen on thrift, Weybourne, 9 June

♂ on green alkanet, 11 June

Worker on green alkanet, Kelling Heath, 1 May

- **FLIGHT** March–September.
- **DISTRIBUTION** Common and widespread.
- **HABITAT** Gardens, hedgerows, grasslands.
- **FLOWERS VISITED** A wide range, but not those with a deep corolla unless nectar robbing. Able to use tiny flowers using the small tongue.
- **NESTING** Uses holes in the ground. Two broods per year.
- **PARASITES** *Bombus sylvestris.*

Bombus ruderarius Red-shanked Carder Bumblebee

Queens and **workers** have black hair with a red tail. They closely resemble *Bombus lapidarius* but can be distinguished by their rounder, shorter abdomen and by the reddish hairs of the pollen basket. **Males** are similar in the two species but the yellow colours are brighter in *B. lapidarius*. The hind tibia is broader in *B.ruderarius* males, with shorter hairs on the hind edge (TB pers. com.). The tongue is quite long.

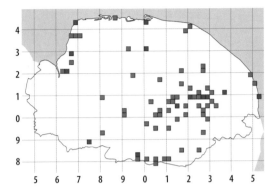

Queen on ground-ivy, Allier Valley, France, 4 April

♂ on field scabious [TB]

Worker on bird's-foot-trefoil, Hayling Island, Hampshire, 3 July

- **FLIGHT** April–August.
- **DISTRIBUTION** This is a scarce and declining species in Britain. It was formerly fairly widespread across south Norfolk. There have been slightly more records in the county in recent years. The nesting cycle is short and the species is probably under-recorded.
- **HABITAT** Breckland rides, brownfield sites, established grasslands.
- **FLOWERS VISITED** Especially Fabaceae and Lamiaceae.
- **NESTING** A carder species using shredded vegetation, sometimes from a disused mouse nest (BWARS).
- **PARASITES** None recorded in the British Isles.

Bombus ruderatus Large Garden Bumblebee

Queens and **workers**: there are three yellow bands, as in *Bombus hortorum*, which it closely resembles, though the head is not quite so long. The tongue is very long. The band on the scutellum is half-moon shaped, with a straight front edge, whereas in *B. hortorum* it is shaped like a crescent moon with a curved front edge. However, both queens and workers often have reduced yellow bands and the band on the abdomen may be entirely absent. The hair on the thorax is short and even. **Males**: some have a similar colour pattern to the yellow form of females but they can also be entirely black. They can be distinguished from *B. hortorum* males by ginger hairs on the mandibles and the acute angle of the hairs on the hind tibia (right angles in *B. hortorum*).

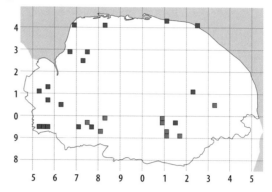

- **FLIGHT** May–August.
- **DISTRIBUTION** Scarce but increasing. Most records come from the Fens but in the past five years it has spread eastwards. Pre-1980 records by Plowright were from the Brecks and the claylands south-west of Norwich where it was found again in 2016 at Ashwellthorpe Wood (TS).
- **HABITAT** Coastal cliffs, rough grassland, gardens, scrub, fenland field and waterway margins.
- **FLOWERS VISITED** Black horehound, ground-ivy, common mallow, white dead-nettle.
- **NESTING** No Norfolk information.
- **PARASITES** *Bombus barbutellus* may be a cuckoo.

Queen, Azores, April

♂ (yellow form) on common mallow, Downham Market, June 2007

Worker on ground-ivy, Muckleburgh, 17 April

♂ (black form) on tufted vetch, Magdalen Hill Down, Hampshire, 8 July

Bombus subterraneus Short-haired Bumblebee

Queens, **workers** and **males** are similar. There is a fairly wide yellow collar and a narrower variable yellow band on the scutellum. The tail is white and the posterior margins of the abdomen segments have brownish-yellow fringes. The hair is very short and the tongue is long.

Queen on viper's-bugloss, New Zealand [NG]

Queen on foxglove, Dungeness [SF]

- ■ **FLIGHT** Probably June–September (BWARS).
- ■ **DISTRIBUTION** The last records in the British Isles were from Kent in 1988, and it was declared extinct in Britain in 2000. Described as "uncommon" by Paget 1834. The last records in Norfolk were apparently in 1923 based on specimens in the NMH collected at Hunstanton by Bridgman and referred to by Plowright. The species was said to be "not uncommon, though by far the rarest of the large Bombi" by Bridgman in his 1889 list.
- ■ **FLOWERS VISITED** The long tongue allows foraging on flowers with deep corollas such as the Fabaceae. Photographs of New Zealand bees derived from British stock show it feeding on viper's-bugloss and red clover.
- ■ **NESTING** In the ground.
- ■ **PARASITES** None known.

Bombus sylvarum Shrill Carder Bumblebee

Queens, **workers** and **males** are similar. The general appearance is of a pale yellow stripy bumblee with an orange-red tail. The yellow hair extends to the top of the head and face. There are black hairs between the wings and one or more blackish bands on the abdomen. The tongue is quite long.

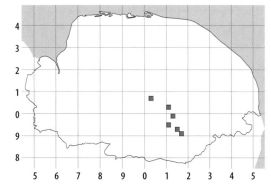

- **FLIGHT** May–September (BWARS).
- **DISTRIBUTION** Considered "common" near Yarmouth by Paget 1834. Described by Bridgman as "very common" in Norfolk in the late 19th century. Plowright found it at six sites between 1960 and 1963 in the clay country southwest of Norwich and these are the last county records. There are some recent signs of population recovery in Kent and Essex.
- **HABITAT** Coastal areas, flower-rich grasslands.
- **FLOWERS VISITED** Include species with a deep corolla such as Lamiaceae.
- **NESTING** Amongst vegetation on the surface or just below ground (BWARS).
- **PARASITES** None known.

Queen on white dead-nettle, France, April

♂ on labiate sp., Beaune, France, September

Bombus terrestris Buff-tailed Bumblebee

Queens are usually very large with a yellow collar, a broad yellow band on the abdomen and a buff tail. There is often a band of buff or peachy-orange where the black meets the whiter tail, or the whole tail can look orange or buff. The yellow bands look more orange than those of the very similar *Bombus lucorum* owing to the inclusion of some black hairs. **Workers** are similar to females but the tip of the abdomen varies from white to buff. **Males** are quite large and look similar to queens, but have orangey-yellow hairs around the (narrower) hind tibia, rather than black. Unlike white-tailed males, they do not have yellow hair on the face or extending under the collar. Queens and males with reduced yellow bands can occur.

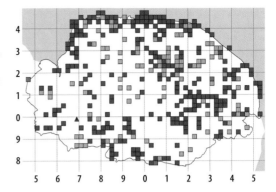

- **FLIGHT** Can be seen in any month but mostly between February and October. It is commonly seen searching for a nest site along hedge banks in the early spring.
- **DISTRIBUTION** One of the most widespread bumblebees in Norfolk and a common visitor to gardens. Coastal areas have particularly strong populations.
- **HABITAT** Occurs in a wide range of habitats, especially open countryside, hedgerows and gardens. In mild winters colonies can be active into November and December, and newly emerged queens may start colonies at this time.
- **FLOWERS VISITED** A very wide range of flowers is used for pollen and nectar. The tongue is fairly short, preventing access to flowers with a deep corolla. However, nectar robbing by biting a hole in the corolla is common. Garden flowers such as *Mahonia* and heathers are used for winter foraging.
- **NESTING** Often uses old mouse holes in grassy places. In recent years nests have been established in winter months.
- **PARASITES** *Bombus vestalis*.

Queen on red clover, Weybourne, 11 June

Worker on weld, Hunworth, June

♂ (dark form) on black knapweed, Swanton Novers Great Wood, 27 August

Bombus barbutellus Barbut's Cuckoo Bumblebee

Females have a yellow collar and untidy yellow hair on the scutellum and first abdominal segment. There are also yellow hairs on the top of the head. The hair on the abdomen is sparse and the tail is white. **Males** are similar to females and this is the only cuckoo bumblebee male with a wholly white tail.

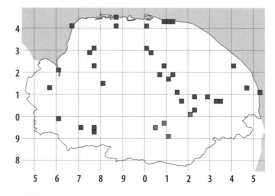

♀ on black knapweed, Swanton Novers Great Wood, 27 August

♂ on spear thistle, Stow Bardolf, 30 June

- **FLIGHT** June–August.
- **DISTRIBUTION** Widespread in the county.
- **HABITAT** As for *Bombus hortorum*.
- **FLOWERS VISITED** Bramble, black knapweed, field scabious, thistles.

- **NESTING** A cuckoo of *B. hortorum* and perhaps *B. ruderatus*.
- **PARASITES** None observed.

Bombus bohemicus Gypsy Cuckoo Bumblebee

Females closely resemble *Bombus vestalis*; both have a yellow collar and yellow flashes at the boundary between the black and white sections of the abdomen. However, the yellow collar is a paler colour in this species and the yellow flashes are less distinct. **Males** are similar to females in colour pattern, and are difficult to distinguish from *B. vestalis*.

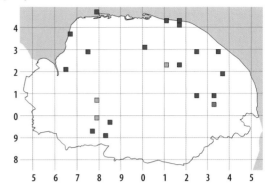

♀ on dandelion, West Tofts, 14 May

♂ on heather, Speyside, Inverness-shire, 19 August

- **FLIGHT** May–August.
- **DISTRIBUTION** Widespread but scarce. Possibly increasing.
- **HABITAT** As for *Bombus lucorum*.

- **FLOWERS VISITED** Especially Asteraceae including dandelion and black knapweed.
- **NESTING** A cuckoo of *Bombus lucorum*.
- **PARASITES** None observed.

Bombus campestris Field Cuckoo Bumblebee

Females have a broad yellow band on the collar and the scutellum, the latter often with a central black division. The abdomen bears very sparse black hairs with the cuticle shining through. T4–T6 have pale buff hairs partly interrupted centrally. **Males** are variable in colour; some are very yellow, having a yellow collar, yellow hairs on the scutellum and yellow hair tufts at the sides of T1. The last three and a half segments also have yellow or brownish hair. Some males are entirely black and there can be darkened intermediates. The hair is uneven in length.

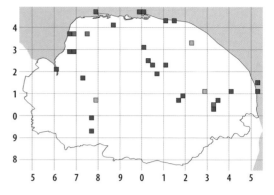

- **FLIGHT** April–September.
- **DISTRIBUTION** Widespread but rather scarce despite the abundance of its host. Seemingly less common than in the 1960s when Plowright described it as the commonest cuckoo bumblebee in Norfolk.
- **HABITAT** As for *Bombus pascuorum*.
- **FLOWERS VISITED** Especially species with many flowers or florets in a cluster.
- **NESTING** A parasite of *B. pascuorum*.
- **PARASITES** None observed.

♀, French Pyrenees, 21 June

♂ (yellow form) on globe thistle, Yarwell, Northamptonshire, 24 July

♂ on field scabious, Eyam Moor, Derbyshire, 21 August

Bombus rupestris Hill Cuckoo Bumblebee

Females are black with a red tail and dark brown wings. Occasionally there can be a yellow collar. **Males** have variable pale bands on the thorax and abdomen. Some are darkened.

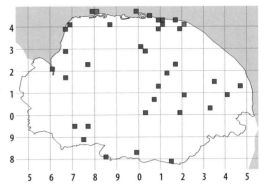

■ **FLIGHT** May–September.
■ **DISTRIBUTION** There is one record from the Aylmerton area 1934 (KD) and from Scolt Head pre-1960 (EAE). The Norfolk population recovered from about the year 2000 and it is now quite frequent.
■ **HABITAT** As for *Bombus lapidarius*.
■ **FLOWERS VISITED** Knapweeds, thistles, viper's-bugloss.
■ **NESTING** A cuckoo of *B. lapidarius*.
■ **PARASITES** None observed.

♀ on spear thistle, Cambridge, August

♂ on greater knapweed, Heydon, Cambridgeshire, 19 June

♀ with yellow collar on bluebell, Swanton Novers Great Wood, 13 May

Bombus sylvestris Forest Cuckoo Bumblebee

Females have a wide pale yellow collar and a white tail. There can be some yellow hairs on the scutellum and front of the abdomen. The tip of the abdomen is pointed and curved down.
Males: the tip of the tail is dark with a red tuft of hair at the very end. There is yellow hair on the top of the head and on the front of the abdomen. There is sometimes yellow at the back of the thorax too. The hair is uneven in length.

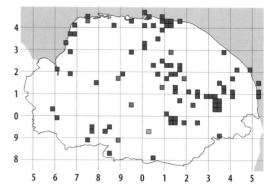

♀, Swanton Novers Great Wood, 23 June

♂ on viper's-bugloss, Stanta, June

- **FLIGHT** Females can be seen in March and April. New females and males appear in early June. There may be a second brood associated with the second brood of its host.
- **DISTRIBUTION** Widespread and fairly common.
- **HABITAT** Hedgerows, gardens, commons, heathland, woodland edge.

- **FLOWERS VISITED** Blackthorn, willows, cotoneaster, dandelion, viper's-bugloss, bell heather, bramble.
- **NESTING** A cuckoo of *Bombus pratorum* and possibly also of the closely related *B. jonellus*.
- **PARASITES** None observed.

Bombus vestalis Vestal Cuckoo Bumblebee

Females are very large with a yellow collar and a lemon-yellow flash at the boundary between the white and black on the abdomen, narrowing at the centre. The cuticle is robust and there is a projecting pointed tip to the abdomen. **Males** are similar in appearance to females but with longer antennae, and there can be some yellow hair on the anterior of the abdomen. This species is very similar to *Bombus bohemicus*. There are differences in the relative length of male antenna segments which can be observed in good photographs: in *B. vestalis* male segment 5 is longer than segment 3 but in *B. bohemicus* these segments are about equal in length.

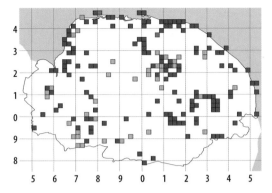

- **FLIGHT** Females come out of hibernation in April and May and new females and males appear in July and August.
- **DISTRIBUTION** This is the most abundant cuckoo bumblebee in Norfolk. It probably occurs in most places where its host is found. Females are seen in the spring searching for host nests, and males can be abundant in midsummer.
- **HABITAT** As for *Bombus terrestris*.
- **FLOWERS VISITED** Females can feed from flowers with quite deep corollas, such as ground-ivy and wood sage. Males favour members of the Asteraceae, such as thistles and knapweeds. Bramble is also frequently used.
- **NESTING** A cuckoo of *B. terrestris*.
- **PARASITES** None observed.

♀ on ground -ivy, Muckleburgh, 17 April

♂ on bramble, Beeston Common, 16 June

APIS – HONEYBEES

The familiar Honeybee comprises one species, *Apis mellifera*, in the British Isles. Most live in hives, but there are some feral bees which originated from domestic stock. There are various genetic strains differing somewhat in colour. All *Apis* species possess a specialised pollen basket on the hind tibiae where a mixture of pollen and nectar is carried. There is a caste system with a queen, workers (sterile females) and males and the species is renowned for its complex social life. Unlike bumblebees, workers survive the winter as a large cluster surrounding the queen and are ready to forage on the first warm days of spring. The tongue is quite short, limiting Honeybees to flowers with a short corolla. Honeybee hives are often placed on nature reserves and other wild places where they potentially compete with native species of bees and other insects.

Worker gathering moisture from moss, Kelling Heath, February

Honeybee nest in a hedge, Shotesham, 21 September [ED]

The brood cells look dark and honey is stored in the pale cells around the edge [ED]

Apis mellifera Honeybee

The **queen** is very large and the workers are also quite large in relation to other British bee species. Nests can contain many thousands of workers. **Workers**: the face is heart shaped with strong triangular mandibles and the eyes are covered in short pale hairs. The clypeus is mostly bare but the top of the head has a crown of black hairs. The forewing is characterised by a long thin marginal cell reaching almost to the wing tip and there are three sub-marginal cells. The thorax and the first two abdominal tergites have long pale brown hairs. The remaining tergites have anterior bands of flattened scale-like white hairs. The anterior tergites have varying amounts of orange colouration with some being entirely dark. The hind tibia is shiny, triangular in shape and fringed with hairs, forming the pollen basket. The hind basitarsus is very broad, the inside being concave and covered in bristles. These are used for collecting pollen from the body hairs and transferring it to the pollen press on the opposite leg. By straightening the hind leg the pollen press pushes pollen up into the pollen basket. **Males (drones)** are broader and larger than workers. Their eyes are very large and meet at the top of the head. The hind tibiae and basitarsi are broad but lack the structures of a pollen basket.

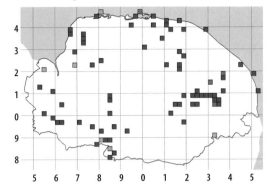

- **FLIGHT** Any time of the year when the weather is suitable.
- **DISTRIBUTION** Widespread and common in the county, but under-recorded.
- **HABITAT** Universal.
- **FLOWERS VISITED** Angelica, apple, blackthorn, bramble, lesser celandine, cherry, cherry plum, crocus, gorse, heather (ling) hellebore, hogweed, ivy, kidney vetch, *Lonicera fragrantissima*, mahonia, phacelia, poppy, sea campion, white bryony, willows, etc.
- **NESTING** Wild nests have been recorded in hollows in oak trees and in a hedge.

Worker, orange form, carrying black poppy pollen, Weybourne, 20 June

Worker, dark form, Weybourne, June

Gardening for bees

Even the smallest garden or window box can provide something for bees. With the loss of flowers in the wider countryside, gardens are playing an increasingly important part in conserving bees.

The main needs of bees are:
- Food (pollen and nectar)
- Nest site (holes in walls, logs and stems, bare earth, snail shells, rough grassland, compost heaps, bird nesting boxes)
- Building materials (mud for mason bees, leaves for leaf-cutters and mastic makers, hairy leaves for wool carders)
- Sunning places (microhabitats where bees can bask, mate and groom)
- Moisture (some bees take up moisture with their tongue, especially Honeybees)

Flowers for bees Big colourful flowers are often not the best for insects. They have been selected for size, and have often lost their nectar and accessible pollen. The best flowers are the old cottage garden varieties, and these will often seed themselves and spread easily. Ideally nectar and pollen sources should be available throughout the season. The following are some suggestions:

Garden flowers for bees (**bold** = good for long-tongued species)

Spring	Midsummer	Late summer
Alkanet	Bellflowers	Globe thistle
Apple	Bird's-foot-trefoil	Goldenrod
Aquilegia	Bramble	Hawkbit
Blackthorn	**Broad bean**	Hebe
Borage	**Catmint**	Ice Plant
Crocus	Cistus (white)	Ivy
Dandelion	**Comfrey**	Knapweed
Daphne	Cat's-ear	Michaelmas-daisy
Dead-nettles	Coneflower	Ragwort
Flowering currant	Cotoneaster	Single aster
Ground-Ivy	**Delphinium**	Sowthistles
Spring heathers	Eryngium	Sunflower
Lungwort	**Foxglove**	Thistles
Mahonia	Geranium	
Primrose	Goldenrod	
Sage	**Hedge woundwort**	
Snowberry	Hogweed	
White clover	**Honeysuckle**	
Willows	Larkspur	
	Lavender	
	Marjoram	
	Red poppies	
	Red clover	
	Runner bean	
	Scabious	
	Yellow loosestrife	
	Weld	

Lasioglossum pauxillum on goldenrod, Weybourne, August

The most likely bumblebee species you will find in your garden are *Bombus lapidarius*, *B. hortorum*, *B. hypnorum*, *B. lucorum*, *B. terrestris*, *B. pratorum*, *B. pascuorum*, *B. vestalis* and *B. sylvestris*. Bumblebee nests last just one season.

B. hortorum and *B. pascorum* have long tongues and specialise in flowers with a deep corolla such as primrose, sage, honeysuckle and foxglove. The queens of short-tongued bumblebees can also use flowers with fairly deep corollas, and short-tongued workers sometimes 'nectar rob' by biting holes in the sides of otherwise inaccessible flowers, for example comfrey and heathers.

Bombus terrestris worker on bell heather, showing holes bitten in the flowers to gain nectar

Honeybees are likely to be common in most gardens, mostly originating from local hives. They may compete with wild bees for food. Bumblebees and Honeybees have a true pollen basket on the hind tibia. Collected pollen moistened with nectar forms a large lump surrounded by long hairs.

Bombus lucorum with full pollen baskets on globe thistle

Megachile sp. bringing pollen to a bee hotel, Weybourne, September

There will be many other bees visiting any garden, most of them solitary species. One of the commonest in the spring is *Anthophora plumipes*. This bee looks rather like a small bumblebee but has a more rapid darting flight. Females are black with orange pollen hairs but males are brown. They visit flowers such as primrose and lungwort.

If a bee 'hotel' is available it is likely to be occupied by several *Osmia* species, especially *O. bicornis*, *O. leaiana* and *O. caerulescens*. Bee hotels are easily made from hollow stems, such as bamboo, bound tightly together and placed horizontally in a sunny place. The ideal diameter varies according to species, so it is best to provide a range from 3 mm to 10 mm. *O. bicornis* uses holes of 7–8 mm and is usually one of the first species to arrive. It is also useful to place some stems vertically since some species prefer this, for example *Hoplitis claviventris*.

A further attraction is to leave some bare ground, perhaps a mound of earth facing the sun, which will attract mining bees such as *Andrena* and *Colletes*.

A survey of Norfolk lawns showed that 40 or more plant species can occur in them. Lawns

A trench and bank prepared for mining bees

A spring lawn with Asteraceae

can easily be managed as bee habitat by cutting in rotation, leaving 3–4 weeks between cuts of some or all of the area. Asteraceae and clovers are particularly useful.

Lastly, it is good to leave some old untreated fence posts or logs in a sunny place to attract hole nesters.

A common garden species, *Andrena bicolor*, on lesser celandine, March

The list below shows the bees recorded in the author's small garden in Weybourne, which overlooks an arable field and from Tim Strudwick's garden in Brundall. Common species are shown in bold.

- ■ ■ **Andrena bicolor**
- ■ ■ *Andrena bimaculata*
- ■ *Andrena chrysosceles*
- ■ *Andrena clarkella*
- ■ ■ **Andrena dorsata**
- ■ *Andrena flavipes*
- ■ ■ **Andrena fulva**
- ■ ■ **Andrena haemorrhoa**
- ■ ■ **Andrena minutula**
- ■ ■ **Andrena nigroaenea**
- ■ ■ **Andrena nitida**
- ■ *Andrena praecox*
- ■ ■ **Andrena scotica**
- ■ *Andrena semilaevis*
- ■ ■ *Andrena synadelpha*
- ■ ■ *Andrena thoracica*
- ■ *Andrena tibialis*
- ■ *Andrena trimmerana*
- ■ ■ *Anthidium manicatum*
- ■ ■ *Anthophora furcata*
- ■ ■ **Anthophora plumipes**
- ■ ■ **Apis mellifera**
- ■ *Bombus bohemicus*
- ■ ■ **Bombus hortorum**
- ■ ■ **Bombus hypnorum**
- ■ *Bombus jonellus*
- ■ ■ **Bombus lapidarius**
- ■ ■ **Bombus lucorum**
- ■ *Bombus muscorum*
- ■ ■ **Bombus pascuorum**
- ■ ■ **Bombus pratorum**
- ■ *Bombus ruderatus*
- ■ **Bombus rupestris**
- ■ ■ **Bombus sylvestris**
- ■ ■ **Bombus terrestris**
- ■ ■ **Bombus vestalis**
- ■ *Coelioxys elongata*
- ■ ■ *Coelioxys inermis*

- ■ ■ *Colletes succinctus*
- ■ *Dasypoda hirtipes*
- ■ *Epeolus cruciger*
- ■ ■ **Halictus tumulorum**
- ■ *Hylaeus brevicornis*
- ■ ■ **Hylaeus communis**
- ■ ■ **Hylaeus hyalinatus**
- ■ ■ **Lasioglossum calceatum**
- ■ *Lasioglossum cupromicans*
- ■ ■ *Lasioglossum leucozonium*
- ■ *Lasioglossum malachurum*
- ■ ■ *Lasioglossum minutissimum*
- ■ ■ **Lasioglossum morio**
- ■ ■ **Lasioglossum parvulum**
- ■ *Lasioglossum pauxillum*
- ■ *Lasioglossum smeathmanellum*
- ■ ■ *Lasioglossum villosulum*
- ■ ■ **Megachile centuncularis**
- ■ ■ **Megachile ligniseca**
- ■ ■ **Megachile willughbiella**
- ■ ■ **Melecta albifrons**
- ■ ■ **Nomada fabriciana**
- ■ ■ **Nomada flava**
- ■ ■ **Nomada flavoguttata**
- ■ *Nomada fucata*
- ■ ■ *Nomada fulvicornis*
- ■ ■ **Nomada goodeniana**
- ■ *Nomada leucophthalma*
- ■ ■ **Nomada marshamella**
- ■ ■ **Nomada panzeri**
- ■ ■ **Nomada ruficornis**
- ■ ■ **Osmia bicornis**
- ■ ■ **Osmia caerulescens**
- ■ ■ **Osmia leaiana**
- ■ *Sphecodes ephippius*
- ■ *Sphecodes monilicornis*
- ■ *Sphecodes niger*
- ■ *Stelis punctulatissima*

■ Author Weybourne   ■ Tim Strudwick Brundall

Photographing bees

Digital photography has revolutionised insect studies. Making a gallery of bee images is an excellent way to get to know them. It is important to label each image with date, locality and grid reference to provide a scientific record which can be submitted to the county recorder. To assist identification it is worth taking images from different perspectives, ideally including profile, face, wing venation and abdomen with wings spread. The flowers visited, season and nesting behaviour can provide further clues.

Some agility is required to get good images of bees visiting flowers in sunny weather. Useful opportunities occur on days with sunny intervals when bees are likely to sit and bask immediately the sun emerges from behind a cloud. Mornings and evenings are also good times. It can be easier to get an image of a bee as it leaves a flower than when it is entering it. The closer the camera to the bee, the less any hand movement will affect the image. A flash is useful in any but the brightest sunny weather. None of the author's images are of chilled or otherwise compromised bees. This can provide detailed images but they rarely look natural. Placing a chilled bee on a flower can give false information about its behaviour.

Andrena fulva ♀ on blackthorn, Oxfordshire, April [PC]

Norfolk's bee recorders

Most of the bee recording in the county has been carried out on an amateur basis rather than by professional scientists. Several have left important collections of bees which have been vital in piecing together historical changes to the bee fauna of the county.

Rev. William Kirby 1759–1850
Born in Suffolk and went to Ipswich School and Cambridge. He worked all his life as a country parson at Barham in Suffolk. He was alive in the time of Linnaeus (1707–1778) and was an original member of the Linnaean Society. Kirby described a large number of new bee species and published *Monographia Apum Angliae* in Ipswich 1802, the first scientific account of British bees. According to Bridgman he lists four species from around Norwich: *Andrena labialis*, *A. dorsata*, *A. barbilabris* and *A. wilkella*.

Charles J Paget and J Paget
Lived at Yarmouth and published *Sketch of the Natural History of Yarmouth and its Neighbourhood* 1834. They listed 22 species of bee from the Yarmouth area including *Bombus distinguendus* (as *B. fragrans*) and *B. subterraneus*.

Frederick Smith 1805–1879
Worked at the British Museum from 1849 publishing lists on the taxonomy of hymenoptera and coleoptera. He visited Norfolk from time to time including Mousehold, publishing a description of the habitat and listing some aculeates observed.

John B Bridgman 1837–1899
A key figure in Norfolk's aculeate recording. He attended Norwich Grammar School then took over his father's dental practice, which he continued for most of his life. He shared his father's interest in conchology but his main interest became Hymenoptera, especially ichneumons and aculeates. He was the Norfolk and Norwich Naturalists' Society's President in 1875, giving his presidential address on 'The Hymenoptera of the Neighbourhood of Norwich'. In 1879 he read a further paper to the Society giving the first county list of 'Chrysididae and Aculeata' comprising 119 species. Additions were published in 1881 and 1889 bringing the total county list to 129 species. Most of his own records came from around the city and he was assisted with identifications by Frederick Smith. He donated his insect collection to the Norwich Castle Museum.

Edward Saunders 1848–1910
Worked in banking and studied entomology in his spare time, mostly in Surrey. He published a beautifully illustrated and comprehensive work on British Bees *The Hymenoptera Aculeata of the British Isles* 1896. He, with his friend the Rev. F D Morice, helped to determine some of the specimens collected by his contemporaries in Norfolk and did some recording in the county. His large aculeate collection is in the Natural History Museum.

Colbran J Wainright 1867–1949
Collected aculeates on a three-week summer stay in West Runton in 1900, recording 27 species, publishing details in *Entomologist* 1901. Bees described as abundant included *Andrena tridentata* (now possibly extinct in the British Isles), the now scarce *A. coitana* and its parasite *Nomada obtusifrons* (the last seen), *Lasioglossum zonulum* (still the only county record) and *Stelis punctulatissimum* (described as "not uncommon").

E A Atmore
A pharmacist in King's Lynn who collected insects in the local area, especially Coleoptera, Hymenoptera and Diptera. He made eight additions to his friend J B Bridgmans's county aculeate list which he reported in *Transactions NNNS* 1909. These include *Andrena argentata* described as "abundant but very local" around King's Lynn and also the only county records of *Nomada roberjeotiana*. His aculeate collection is in the Norwich Castle Museum.

R C (Chris) Plowright
Made pioneering studies of Norfolk's bumblebees in the 1960s. He moved to Norfolk in 1960 when newly married and lived at Wacton with his bee hives while teaching biology at Norwich School. His first interest was ornithology but while teaching spent his spare time scouring Norfolk for bumblebees, being the last to record *Bombus humilis* and *B. sylvarum* in the county. From 1960–1964 he visited 147 county sites making lists of species found. He carried out censuses of queen bumblebees to assess their relative abundance and produced distribution maps, publishing his findings in *Transactions NNNS* 1967. He emigrated to Canada with his wife and young daughter in 1964 to pursue a PhD at the University of Manitoba. Thereafter he has published many further papers on bumblebees. His bumblebee collection is in the Norwich Castle Museum.

Ken Durrant 1920–2010
Brought up in Cromer and spent much of his working life in Dereham where he raised his family, before returning to Sheringham on retirement. He worked in telecommunications, latterly British Telecom. He was an outstanding all round naturalist with a particular interest in insects, always ready to share his enthusiasm and knowledge with others. He was very active with the NNNS and was President twice. Records of note include *Andrena coitana*, *A. fucata*, *A. tarsata* and *Bombus humilis*. He donated his large insect collection to the Norwich Castle Museum.

Peter Yeo 1929–2010
Worked for 40 years as a plant taxonomist at Cambridge Botanic Garden from 1953. He collected aculeates from 1949 to 2003 and made several visits to Norfolk. Particular finds include *Andrena argentata* at Sandringham Warren in 1954. His collection is at the David Attenborough Building at Cambridge Zoology Department.

Tony Irwin
Worked for many years as Curator of Natural History at the Norwich Castle Museum. His speciality is Diptera, but he has great expertise in all insects, birds and other taxa. He was one of the few people recording Norfolk's aculeates in the second half of the 20th century, with records including *Andrena fucata*, *Anthophora quadrimaculata*, *Nomada argentata* and (recently) *Lasioglossum sexnotatum*.

David Richmond
Worked in NHS management information services in Norfolk until his retirement in 2008. He has been county orthoptera recorder from 1990

and bumblebee recorder from 1996, publishing accounts of both groups in 2001 as part of NNNS Wildlife 2000 project. As county recorder he has provided regular updates on these groups in *Transactions of NNNS*, and provided the distribution maps for *Bumblebees of Norfolk* 2012.

Geoff Nobes
A major contributor to Norfolk's aculeate records this century, records coming especially from his large garden at Carbrooke near Watton and from other parts of the Brecks. Notable finds include *Andrena tarsata*, *Stelis ornatula*, *S. phaeoptera*, *Nomada flavopicta* and *Lasioglossum prasinum*.

Ash Murray
Based at Wolferton where he is Senior Reserves Manager for Natural England, with a special interest in bats and bumblebees. He has also provided many records of other bees. Notable finds include *Bombus monticola* at Scolt and *Andrena lapponica* at Dersingham Bog.

Tim Strudwick
Based at Brundall. Site Manager of the Mid-Yare National Nature Reserve for the RSPB since 2003. In the early 2000s began a project to update our knowledge of the county's aculeates, and has contributed the majority of records to the county database this century. As County Recorder he has validated records and gleaned further data from collections at Norwich Castle Museum. He has passed on his knowledge and enthusiasm to many others, including the author, resulting in a new surge of interest in bees and wasps in the county. In 2012 he published *The bees of Norfolk: a provisional county list* in *Transactions of NNNS* which provides the groundwork for this book.

Bibliography

Allen, Geoff (2009) *Bees, wasps and ants of Kent. A provisional atlas*. Kent Field Club.

Atmore, E A (1909) Fauna and Flora of Norfolk Part IX, Hymenoptera – additions. *Trans. Norfolk Norwich Nat. Soc.* 8, 821–825

Baldock, David W (2008) *Bees of Surrey*. Surrey Wildlife Trust.

Barnes, Gerry and Williamson, Tom (2015) *Rethinking Ancient Woodland. The archaeology and history of woods in Norfolk*. University of Hertfordshire Press.

Beckett, Gillian, Bull, Alec and Stevenson, Robin (1999) *A Flora of Norfolk*. Jarrold Book Printing.

Benton, Ted (2006) *Bumblebees*. New Naturalist No 98. Collins.

Benton, Ted (2017) *Solitary Bees*. Naturalists' Handbooks 33 Ecology and Identification.

Bridgman, J B (1876) Presidential Address. *Trans. Norfolk Norwich Nat. Soc.* 2, 111–124.

Bridgman, J B (1876) Notes on the aculeate Hymenoptera. *Trans. Norfolk Norwich Nat. Soc.* 2, 275–279.

Bridgman, J B (1879) Flora and Fauna of Norfolk Part IX, Hymenoptera. *Trans. Norfolk Norwich Nat. Soc.* 2, 617–638.

Bridgman, J B (1881) Flora and Fauna of Norfolk Part IX, Hymenoptera. *Trans. Norfolk Norwich Nat. Soc.* 3, 367–368.

Bridgman, J B (1889) Flora and Fauna of Norfolk Part IX, Hymenoptera – additions. *Trans. Norfolk Norwich Nat. Soc.* 4, 690–691.

Brock, Paul D (2014) *A comprehensive guide to Insects of Britain and Ireland*. Pisces Publications.

Buglife B-lines Norfolk: https://www.buglife.org.uk/sites/default/files/Norfolk%20B-Lines%20farmer%20leaflet.pdf.

Bull, A (2015) *Looking at Brambles*. Catton Print, Norwich.

De Zylva, Paul (2016) *Is Ragwort Poisonous? A Ragwort Myth-buster*. Friends of the Earth. www.foe.co.uk/nature/ragwort.

Dobson, H E M (1987) Role of flower and pollen aromas in host-plant recognition by solitary bees. *Oecologia* (Berlin) 72 618–623.

Dolman, P M, Panter, C J. and Mossman, H L (2010) *Securing Biodiversity in Breckland: Guidance for Conservation and Research*. First Report of the Breckland Biodiversity Audit. University of East Anglia, Norwich.

Edwards, M and Else, G. (In prep.) *Handbook of the Bees of the British Isles*. Ray Society.

Ellis, Bob (2017) Muckweed, Sandweed and Buddle: a survey of arable plants in Norfolk carried out between 2007 and 2012. Presidential Address. *Trans. Norfolk Norwich Nat. Soc.* in press.

Fabre, J H (1918) *The Wonders of Instinct*. T Fisher Unwin, London.

Falk, Steven and Lewington, Richard (2015) *Field Guide to the Bees of Great Britain and Ireland*. British Wildlife Field Guides, Bloomsbury.

Field, J P and Foster, W A (1988) The bees and wasps of Scolt Head Island National Nature Reserve Norfolk. *British Journal of Entomology and Natural History* 1 79-83

Freeman, R B (1968) Charles Darwin on the routes of male humble bees. *Bulletin of the British Museum (Natural History)* Historical Series 3 (6).

Goulson, Dave (2013) *A Sting in the Tale*. Jonathan Cape London.

Goulson, Dave (2014) *A Buzz in the Meadow*. Jonathan Cape London.

Jacobs, Jennifer H, *et al.* (2009) Pollination biology of fruit-bearing hedgerow plants and the role of flower-visiting insects in fruit-set. *Annals of Botany* 104, 1397–1404.

Jones, Nigel and Cheeseborough, Ian (2014) *A provisional atlas of the bees, wasps and ants of Shropshire*. Field Studies Council.

Jukes, Andy (2016) *Andrena nigrospina* and *Andrena pilipes*: where we are now. *BWARS Newsletter* Autumn.

Kleijn, David, *et al.* (2015) Delivery of crop pollination services is an insufficient argument for wild pollinator conservation. http://www.nature.com/articles/ncomms8414.

Kirk, William D J (2006) *A colour guide to pollen loads of the honey bee*. International Bee Research Association.

Kirk, W D and Howes, F N (2012) *Plants for bees: a guide to the plants that benefit bees in the British Isles*. International Bee Research Association.

Miller-Struttmann, N E, *et al.* (2015) Functional mismatch in a bumblebee pollination mutualism. *Science* 349 1541–1544.

Múller, Andreas and Kuhlmann, Michael (2008) Pollen hosts of western palearctic bees of the genus *Colletes* (Hymenoptera: Colletidae): the Asteraceae paradox. *Biological Journal of the Linnaean Society* 95 (4) 719–733.

Nobes, Geoff (2015) *Colletes cunicularius* new to Norfolk. *BWARS Newsletter* Autumn 24-25.

Nowakowski, M and Pywell, R F (2016) *Habitat Creation and Management for Pollinators*. Centre for Ecology & Hydrology, Wallingford, UK.

Oddy, Lizzie (2016) *State of the Natural Environment in Norfolk.* Norfolk Biodiversity Information Service, Norfolk County Council.

O'Toole, Christopher (2013) *Bees, A Natural History.* Nevraumont Publishing Company & Firefly Books.

Owens, N W (2011) Some observations on sallow catkin visitors. *Trans. Norfolk Norwich Nat. Soc.* 44(1) 65-68.

Owens, N W (2013) What good is Alexanders? *The Norfolk Natterjack* 120, 3.

Owens, Nick (2011) How far does a bee fly? Some observations of bumblebee dispersal in Norfolk. *Trans. Norfolk Norwich Nat. Soc.* 42 (1) 46–47.

Owens, Nick (2013) Bee and Wasp records from Blakeney Point. *Trans. Norfolk Norwich Nat. Soc.* 46 (1) 94–8.

Owens, Nick and Richmond, David (2012) *Bumblebees of Norfolk.* Occasional Publication No. 14, Norfolk Norwich Nat. Soc.

Paget, C J and Paget J (1834) *Sketch of the Natural History of Yarmouth and its Neighbourhood.* Yarmouth: F Skill.

Plowright, R C (1967) On the distribution of bumblebees in Norfolk. *Trans. Norfolk Norwich Nat. Soc.* 21, 48–88.

Plowright, R C and Stephen, W P (1973) A numerical taxonomic analysis of the evolutionary relationships of *Bombus* and *Psithyrus* (Apidae: Hymenoptera). *Canadian Entomologist* 105 (5), 733–743.

Plowright, C M S and Plowright, R C (2008) Further evidence for the replacement of *Bombus muscorum* (L) by *Bombus pascuorum* (Scop.) in northern Britain. *Entomologist's Monthly Magazine* 145 1–6.

Praz, Christophe J, Múller, Andreas and Dorn, Silvia (2008) Specialised bees fail to develop on non-host pollen: do plants chemically protect their pollen? *Ecology* 89 (3) 795–804.

Proctor, Michael and Yeo, Peter (1973) *The Pollination of Flowers,* New Naturalist, Collins.

Prys-Jones, O E and Corbet, S A (2011) *Bumblebees* (3rd Ed). Naturalists' Handbooks No 6. Pelagic Publishing, Exeter.

Shaw, J M (1996) Heath Topic Paper, Consultation Draft. Norfolk County Council.

Sladen, F W L (1912) *The Humble-bee its life history and how to domesticate it.* Reprinted Logaston Press 1989.

Smith, Frederick (1868) Notes on Hymenoptera. *Entomologists Annual* 81–96.

Stevan (2015) Visual and Olfactory Cues of *Campanula* (Campanulaceae) and their Significance for Host Recognition by an Oligolectic Bee Pollinator. http://dx.doi.org/10.1371/journal.pone.0128577.

Strudwick, Tim (2011) The bees of Norfolk: a provisional county list. *Trans. Norfolk Norwich Nat. Soc.* 44 (1) 36–56.

Strudwick, Tim (2015) Wildlife Report 2012–2014 Solitary bees and aculeate wasps. *Trans. Norfolk Norwich Nat. Soc.* 48 (1) 69–75,

Wainwright, C J (1901) Diptera and Hymenoptera in Norfolk. *Entomologist* 34 201–203.

SOCIETIES FOR BEES
Bees Wasps and Ants Recording Society
http://www.bwars.com
Buglife https://www.buglife.org.uk
Bumblebee Conservation Trust
http://bumblebeeconservation.org
Norfolk and Norwich Naturalists' Society
http://www.nnns.org.uk
Norfolk Wildlife Trust
https://www.norfolkwildlifetrust.org.uk
Royal Society for the Protection of Birds
https://www.rspb.org.uk

Initials and acronyms

Initials of those referred to in the text

MA	Michael Archer
DB	David Baldock
JB	Jeremy Bartlett
TB	Ted Benton
DC	Dorothy Cheyne
EC	Ed Cross
KD	Ken Durrant
JE	Jeremy Early
EAE	Ted Ellis
GE	George Else
SF	Steven Falk
FF	Francis Farrow
MF	Michael Fogden
JF	John Furse
PH	Peter Harvey
TH	Tim Hodge
TI	Tom Ings
AI	Tony Irwin
AM	Ash Murray
AMg	Andy Musgrove
GN	Geoff Nobes
SP	Stuart Paston
PS	Paddy Saunders
TS	Tim Strudwick
RT	Roger Tidman
TW	Tom Wood
PY	Peter Yeo

Acronyms used in text

NHM	Natural History Museum London
BWARS	Bees Wasps and Ants Recording Society
NBIS	Norfolk Biodiversity Information Service
NCM	Norwich Castle Museum
NE	Natural England
NNNS	Norfolk and Norwich Naturalists' Society
NWT	Norfolk Wildlife Trust
RSPB	Royal Society for the Protection of Birds

Photographic credits

AC	Amanda Crudgington
AJ	Adrian Jones
CW	Catherine Winget
DO	Darren Oddy
ED	Elizabeth Dack
GE	George Else
JF	John Furse
MF	Michael Fogden
MG	Martin Greenland
NG	Nikki Gammans
NS	Neil Sherman
PB	Paul Brock
PC	Peter Creed
PS	Paddy Saunders
RGC	Ramón Gomez de la Cuesta
RT	Roger Tidman
SF	Steven Falk
TB	Ted Benton
TC	Tim Cowan
TMcK	Tony McKie
TS	Tim Strudwick

Appendix 1: *Andrena* habitats in Norfolk

The table shows the *Andrena* species recorded at various Norfolk sites, colour coded to show the major habitat type at each site. The most widespread species were *A. bicolor*, *A. dorsata*, *A. haemorrhoa*, *A. minutula* and *A. nigroaenea*. Only *A. haemorrhoa* was seen on the shingle ridge of Blakeney Point, otherwise these species occurred in all habitat categories. *A. haemorrhoa* is also the only strictly single brooded of the five most widespread species. The most diverse habitats were heathland (with scrub), this habitat lacking only some grassland specialists.

Key:　█ Dunes;　█ Heathland;　█ Chalk grassland;　█ Brecks, acidic & alkaline heaths;
　　　█ Woodland;　█ River valley dry woodland;　█ Gardens;　█ Coatal cliffs & quarries;　█ Fens

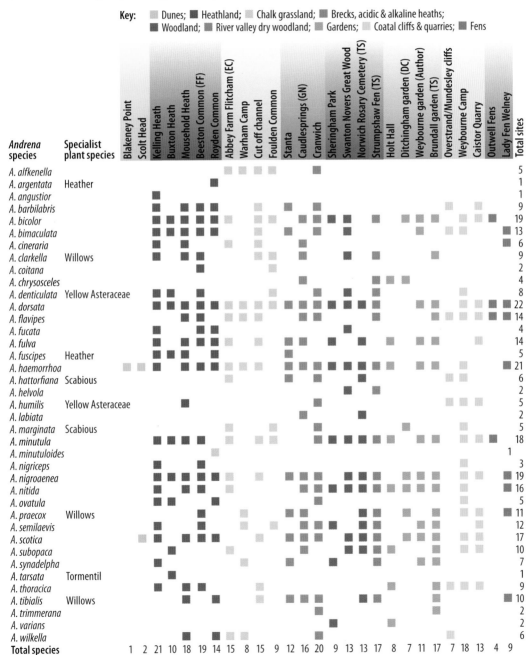

Appendix 2: 19th and early 20th century bees list, Bridgman and Atmore

John Bridgman was the first to compile a list of Norfolk's bees which he published in *Transactions of NNNS* in 1879. He made some additions over the next few years and more species were added by E A Atmore in 1909, making a total of about 140 species. Sixteen of these species are now probably extinct in the county and 12 species have considerably declined based on the authors' notes about their former abundance. Key: **red** = not recorded since 1909; **green** = declined since 19th century.

Present name	Bridgman	Authors' notes
Andrena angustior	*Andrena angustior*	Single female Mousehold (Bridgman 1879)
A. barbilabris	*A. albicrus*	Generally distributed and common April–May (Bridgman 1879)
A. trimmerana?	*A. picicornis*	Very local, Mousehold and Cringleford April (Bridgman 1879)
A. bicolor	*A. gwynana*	Very abundant in early spring...principally on dandelion (Bridgman 1879)
A. bicolor (second brood)	*A. bicolor*	Not uncommon Norwich June and July (Bridgman 1879)
A. bimaculata (?form with no red)	*A. vitrea*	Far from common, Mousehold and Brundall, July (Bridgman 1879)
A. bimaculata (first brood)	*A. bimaculata*	Local but numerous Norwich, Brundall April (Bridgman 1879)
A. bimaculata (summer brood)	*A. decorata*	Plentiful round Norwich, Brundall and Costessey, end of July and August (Bridgman 1879)
A. chrysosceles	*A. chrysosceles*	Specimens from Carbrooke (Bridgman 1879)
A. clarkella	*A. clarkella*	From Paget, Yarmouth (Bridgman 1879)
A. coitana	*A. coitana*	Not uncommon round the city. Plentiful Brundall July and August (Bridgman 1879)
A. dorsata (?summer brood)	*A. dorsata*	Common on bramble flowers July and August (Bridgman 1879)
A. dorsata (spring brood)	*A. combinata = A. collinsonana*	Willows at Norwich and Brundall April (Bridgman 1879)
A. flavipes	*A. fulvicrus*	One male from Brundall (Bridgman 1879)
A. fucata	*A. fucata*	One female Carbrooke (Bridgman 1879)
A. haemorrhoa	*A. albicans*	Very common everywhere (Bridgman 1879)
A. hattorfiana	*A. hattorfiana*	July 1876 at Eaton and Worstead at the flowers of *Knautia arvensis* (Bridgman 1879)
A. helvola	*A. helvola*	Common in the neighbourhood of the city April–June (Bridgman 1879)
A. labialis	*A. labialis*	Not common Eaton, Harford Bridges, Brundall, Yarmouth, Lynn, June (Bridgman 1879)
A. labiata	*A. cingulata*	Not uncommon . . . in the neighbourhood of Norwich (Bridgman 1879)
A. marginata	*A. cetii*	Eaton (Bridgman 1879)
A. minutula	*A. parvula*	Very common from March (Bridgman 1879)
A. minutuloides	*A. minutula*	Far from common (Bridgman 1879)
A. nigroaenea	*A. nigro-aenea*	Perhaps the most common . . . species of the genus (Bridgman 1879)
A. nigroaenea male?	*A. aprilina*	One male (Bridgman 1879)
A. nitida	*A. nitida*	Far from common around Norwich April–June (Bridgman 1879)
A. nitida?	*A. pubescens*	Mousehold . . . flowers of the heath August (Bridgman 1879)
A. ovatula (black legged form)	*A. afzeliella*	Common April, May and end of July (Bridgman 1879)
A. ovatula (red legged form)	*A. fuscata*	Mousehold April, May (Bridgman 1879)
A. pilipes (s.l.)	*A. pilipes*	Occasionally taken around Norwich, end of May and June (Bridgman 1879)
A. praecox	*A. smithella*	Plenty at flowers of willow Norwich, Brundall (Bridgman 1879)
A. semilaevis	*A. nana*	Not uncommon (Bridgman 1879)
A. thoracica	*A. thoracica*	Generally distributed around Norwich, Brundall, Wroxham (Bridgman 1879)
A. tibialis	*A. atriceps*	Very abundant on willows [early spring] (Bridgman 1879)
A. tridentata	*A. tridentata*	Not uncommon at ragwort in July (males) (Bridgman 1879)
A. trimmerana	*A. trimmerana*	Fairly common around Norwich (Bridgman 1879)
A. varians	*A. varians*	Less common than *A. helvola* April–June (Bridgman 1879)
A. wilkella	*A. convexiuscula = A. xanthura*	Plentiful in neighbourhood of Norwich April–June (Bridgman 1879)
Anthidium manicatum	*Anthidium manicatum*	Abounds in mid-summer (Bridgman 1879)
Anthophora furcata	*Anthophora furcata*	Not uncommon Eaton, Earlham, Mousehold, Brundall from May–June (Bridgman 1879)
A. plumipes	*A. acervorum*	In almost every dry bank (Bridgman 1879)
A. retusa	*A. retusa*	Plentiful Mousehold and neighbourhood usually beginning of May (Bridgman 1879)
Apis mellifera	*Apis mellifera*	(Bridgman 1879)

Present name	Bridgman	Authors' notes
Bombus barbutellus	*Bombus barbutellus*	Very abundant (Bridgman 1879)
B. campestris	*B. campestris*	Males plentiful but females far from common (Bridgman 1879)
B. distinguendus	*B. elegans*	Far from common, Mousehold, Yarmouth, Brundall, Cromer (Bridgman 1879)
B. hortorum	*B. hortorum*	To be found everywhere (Bridgman 1879)
B. humilis	*B. venustus*	Not uncommon (Bridgman 1879)
B. jonellus	*B. jonellus*	Two from near Norwich, apparently scarce (Bridgman 1879)
B. lapidarius	*B. lapidarius*	To be found everywhere (Bridgman 1879)
B. lucorum	*B. lucorum*	To be found everywhere (Bridgman 1879)
B. muscorum	*B. muscorum*	Very abundant (Bridgman 1879)
B. pascuorum	*B. agrorum*	Neighbourhood of Norwich (Bridgman 1879)
B. pratorum	*B. pratorum*	Very abundant (Bridgman 1879)
B. rupestris	*B. rupestris*	Very abundant (Bridgman 1879)
B. subterraeneus	*B. subterraeneus*	Tolerably abundant (Bridgman 1879)
B. sylvarum	*B. sylvarum*	Very common (Bridgman 1879)
B. ruderarius	*B. dermahellus*	Not uncommon (Bridgman 1879)
B. terrestris	*B. virginalis*	To be found everywhere (Bridgman 1879)
B. vestalis	*B. vestialis*	Very abundant (Bridgman 1879)
Chelostoma campanularum	*Chelostoma campanularum*	Abounds in gardens in Norwich on *Campanula* (Bridgman 1879)
C. florisomne	*C. florisomne*	Harford bridges June–July (Bridgman 1879)
Coelioxys elongata	*Coelioxys simplex*	Very abundant in June, July (Bridgman 1879)
C. inermis	*C. acuminata*	Not uncommon (Bridgman 1879)
C. quadridentata	*C. quadridentata*	Not uncommon in June, Eaton, Postwick. Also Yarmouth and at Bawsey Heath 10th Sept 1877 (Bridgman 1879)
C. rufescens	*C. rufescens*	Less common than other *Coelioxys* (Bridgman 1879)
Colletes daviesanus	*Colletes daviesana*	In almost every sandy bank (Bridgman 1879)
C. fodiens	*C. fodiens*	[Several sites on Ragwort] (Bridgman 1879)
C. succinctus	*C. succincta*	Abundant on Mousehold at the flowers of the heath (Bridgman 1879)
Dasypoda hirtipes	*Dasypoda hirtipes*	Recorded near Yarmouth (Bridgman 1879)
Epeolus variegatus	*Epeolus variegatus*	Common at burrows of *Colletes daviesana* (Bridgman 1879)
Eucera longicornis	*Eucera longicornis*	Not uncommon round Norwich. Large colony at Postwick, from end of May (Bridgman 1879)
Halictus rubicundus	*Halictus rubicundus*	Not uncommon (Bridgman 1879)
Hylaeus communis	*Prosopis communis*	Commonest species of the genus (Bridgman 1879)
H. confusus	*Hylaeus confusus*	Not common; at the flowers of the bramble (Bridgman 1879)
H. hyalinatus	*H. hyalinatus*	Rather common (Bridgman 1879)
H. pictipes	*Prosopis varipes*	One male in the neighbourhood of Norwich (Bridgman 1879)
H. signatus	*H. signatus*	Generally to be found at the flowers of the mignonette (Bridgman 1879)
H. sp. = ?	*Prosopis perforata*	Occasionally taken at the flowers of the bramble, Earlham (Bridgman 1879)
Lasioglossum albipes	*Halictus albipes*	Very common (Bridgman 1879)
L. calceatum	*H. cyclindricus*	Very common (Bridgman 1879)
L. fulvicornis	*H. fulvicornis*	Recorded at Cromer (Bridgman 1879)
L. leucopus	*H. aeratus = H. leucopus*	Very common (Bridgman 1879)
L. leucozonium	*H. leucozonius*	Very common (Bridgman 1879)
L. malachurum	*H. malachurus*	Recorded at Cromer (Bridgman 1879)
L. minutissiumum	*H. minutissimum*	Very common (Bridgman 1879)
L. morio	*H. morio*	Very common (Bridgman 1879)
L. nitidiusculum	*H. nitidiusculus*	Generally distributed (Bridgman 1879)
L. parvulum	*H. minutus*	Generally distributed (Bridgman 1879)
L. punctatissimum	*H. longiceps*	Norwich (Bridgman 1879)
L. quadrinotatum	*H. quadrinotatus*	Tolerably abundant (Bridgman 1879)
L. smeathmanellum	*H. smeathmanellus*	Occasional Norwich, Brundall, Cromer (Bridgman 1879)
L. villosulum	*H. villosulus*	Cromer and not uncommon round Norwich (Bridgman 1879)
Macropis europaea	*Macropis labiata*	Brundall taking pollen from *Lysimachia* (Bridgman 1879)
Megachile centuncularis	*Megachile centuncularis*	Very common in gardens and at bramble flowers June–August (Bridgman 1879)
M. circumcincta	*M. circumcincta*	Not uncommon around the city June–July (Bridgman 1879)
M. ligniseca	*M. ligniseca*	Reported by Paget (Bridgman 1879)
M. maritima	*M. maritima*	Not uncommon Mousehold, Yarmouth (Bridgman 1879)
M. versicolor	*M. versicolor*	One record Bridgman's garden Norwich (Bridgman 1879)
M. willughbiella	*M. willughbiella*	By far the most plentiful species of the genus June–August (Bridgman 1879)
Melecta albifrons	*Melecta armata*	Very common at burrows of *Anthophora acervorum* (Bridgman 1879)

Present name	Bridgman	Authors' notes
Melitta haemorrhoidalis	*Cilissa haemorrhoidalis*	Not uncommon at flowers of *Campanula* July, August (Bridgman 1879)
M. leporina	*C. leporina*	Occasional July, August at Brundall at flowers of white clover (Bridgman 1879)
Nomada armata	*Nomada armata*	Three females Eaton July 1876 (Bridgman 1879)
N. ferruginata	*N. lateralis*	Brundal, Cringleford April–May (Bridgman 1879)
N. flavoguttata	*N. flavo-guttata*	King's Lynn: Atmore (Bridgman 1879)
N. flavopicta	*N. jacobaeae*	Rather plentiful July–August 1874 otherwise far from common (Bridgman 1879)
N. fulvicornis	*N. lineola*	Mousehold May–June (Bridgman 1879)
N. goodeniana	*N. succincta*	Very common end of April–June (Bridgman 1879)
N. lathburiana	*N. alternata*	Very common end of April–June (Bridgman 1879)
N. obtusifrons	*N. obtusifrons*	Brundall July, August on creeping thistles (Bridgman 1879)
N. ruficornis	*N. ruficornis*	Very common May–June (Bridgman 1879)
N. rufipes	*N. solidaginis*	Extremely plentiful at Ragwort July–August (Bridgman 1879)
N. sexfasciata	*N. sexfasciata*	At *Eucera* site near Thorpe May–June (Bridgman 1879)
N. sheppardana	*N. furva*	Non uncommon at burrows of small Halicti May–June (Bridgman 1879)
N. striata	*N. ochrostoma*	Females at Eaton and Earlham June (Bridgman 1879)
Osmia bicornis	*Osmia rufa*	Very abundant early spring (Bridgman 1879)
O. caerulescens	*O. aenaea*	Not uncommon end April–June (Bridgman 1879)
O. leaiana	*O. fulviventris*	Norwich, Eaton, Harford Bridges, Brundall June–July (Bridgman 1879)
O. spinulosa	*O. spinulosa*	Brundall, scarce (Bridgman 1879)
Panurgus banksianus	*Panurgus banksianus*	Abundant Mousehold and Eaton June–August (Bridgman 1879)
Sphecodes ephippius	*Sphecodes ephippius*	Very common (Bridgman 1879)
S. gibbus	*S. gibbus*	Generally distributed, common (Bridgman 1879)
S. monilicornis	*S. subquadratus*	Few specimens (Bridgman 1879)
S. rubicundus	*S. rufiventris*	Generally distributed, common (Bridgman 1879)
Stelis punctulatissima	*Stelis aterrima*	In Bridgman's garden Norwich July (Bridgman 1879)
Andrena tarsata	*Andrena analis*	Male at Felthorpe (Bridgman 1881)
Colletes similis	*Colletes picistigma*	Female Unthank Road Norwich (Bridgman 1881)
Stelis phaeoptera	*Stelis phaeoptera*	One on thistles at Brundall 10th August 1897 (Bridgman 1881)
Sphecodes crassus	*Sphecodes variegatus*	(Bridgman 1889)
S. ephippius	*S. similis*	[?but reported as *S. ephippius* 1879] (Bridgman 1889)
S. ferruginatus	*S. ferruginatus*	One female at Brundall (Bridgman 1889)
S. geoffrellus	*S. affinis*	(Bridgman 1889)
S. miniatus	*S. dimidiatus*	Appears to be common (Bridgman 1889)
S. pellucidus	*S. pilifrons*	(Bridgman 1889)
S. puncticeps	*S. puncticeps*	One male (Bridgman 1889)
Osmia pilicornis	*Osmia pilicornis*	One record (Atmore 1899)
Andrena argentata	*Andrena argentata*	King's Lynn area, abundant but very local (Atmore 1909)
A. denticulata	*A. denticulata*	King's Lynn area, frequent on *Calluna vulgaris* (Atmore 1909)
A. niveata	*A. niveata*	King's Lynn area, two specimens (Atmore 1909)
A. synadelpha	*A. ambigua*	King's Lynn area, several specimens (Atmore 1909)
Hoplitis claviventris	*Osmia leucomelana*	King's Lynn area, nine specimens on *Lotus corniculatus* (Atmore 1909)
Nomada fabriciana	*Nomada fabriciana*	King's Lynn area, scarce (Atmore 1909)
N. roberjeotiana	*N. roberjeotiana*	King's Lynn area, July–August on Ragwort (Atmore 1909)
N. ruficornis	*N. bifida*	King's Lynn area, not uncommon (Atmore 1909)

Appendix 3: Norfolk list

A total of 197 bee species have been recorded in Norfolk since records began in the 19th century. Of these 174 have been recorded post-2000.

	Post-2000		Post-2000		Post-2000		Post-2000
Andrena alfkenella	✓	Bombus barbutellus	✓	H. signatus	✓	N. panzeri	✓
A. angustior	✓	B. bohemicus	✓	Lasioglossum albipes	✓	N. roberjeotiana	
A. argentata	✓	B. campestris	✓	L. brevicorne	✓	N. ruficornis	✓
A. barbilabris	✓	B. distinguendus		L. calceatum	✓	N. rufipes	✓
A. bicolor	✓	B. hortorum	✓	L. cupromicans	✓	N. sexfasciata	
A. bimaculata	✓	B. humilis		L. fratellum		N. sheppardana	✓
A. chrysosceles	✓	B. hypnorum	✓	L. fulvicorne	✓	N. signata	✓
A. cineraria	✓	B. jonellus	✓	L. lativentre	✓	N. striata	✓
A. clarkella	✓	B. lapidarius	✓	L. leucopus	✓	Osmia aurulenta	✓
A. coitana	✓	B. lucorum s.l.	✓	L. leucozonium	✓	O. bicolor	✓
A. denticulata	✓	B. monticola	✓	L. malachurum	✓	O. bicornis	✓
A. dorsata	✓	B. muscorum	✓	L. minutissimum	✓	O. caerulescens	✓
A. flavipes	✓	B. pascuorum	✓	L. morio	✓	O. leaiana	✓
A. fucata	✓	B. pratorum	✓	L. nitidiusculum	✓	O. pilicornis	
A. fulva	✓	B. ruderarius	✓	L. parvulum	✓	O. spinulosa	✓
A. fuscipes	✓	B. ruderatus	✓	L. pauperatum		Panurgus banksianus	✓
A. haemorrhoa	✓	B. rupestris	✓	L. pauxillum		P. calcaratus	✓
A. hattorfiana	✓	B. subterraneus		L. prasinum	✓	Sphecodes crassus	✓
A. helvola	✓	B. sylvarum		L. punctatissimum	✓	S. ephippius	✓
A. humilis	✓	B. sylvestris	✓	L. puncticolle	✓	S. ferruginatus	
A. labialis		B. terrestris		L. quadrinotatum	✓	S. geoffrellus	
A. labiata	✓	B. vestalis	✓	L. sexnotatum	✓	S. gibbus	
A. lapponica	✓	Chelostoma campanularum	✓	L. smeathmanellum	✓	S. hyalinatus	
A. marginata	✓	C. florisomne	✓	L. villosulum	✓	S. longulus	
A. minutula	✓	Coelioxys conoidea	✓	L. xanthopus		S. miniatus	
A. minutuloides	✓	C. elongata	✓	L. zonulum	✓	S. monilicornis	
A. nigriceps	✓	C. inermis	✓	Macropis europaea	✓	S. niger	
A. nigroaenea	✓	C. quadridentata		Megachile centuncularis	✓	S. pellucidus	
A. nigrospina	✓	C. rufescens	✓	M. circumcincta	✓	S. puncticeps	
A. nitida	✓	Colletes cunicularius		M. leachella	✓	S. reticulatus	
A. niveata		C. daviesanus	✓	M. ligniseca	✓	S. rubicundus	
A. ovatula	✓	C. fodiens	✓	M. maritima	✓	S. spinulosus	✓
A. pilipes	✓	C. halophilus	✓	M. versicolor	✓	Stelis ornatula	✓
A. praecox	✓	C. hederae	✓	M. willughbiella	✓	S. phaeoptera	✓
A. proxima		C. marginatus	✓	Melecta albifrons	✓	S. punctulatissima	✓
A. scotica	✓	C. similis	✓	Melitta leporina	✓		
A. semilaevis	✓	C. succinctus	✓	M. haemorrhoidalis	✓		
A. simillima		Dasypoda hirtipes	✓	M. tricincta	✓		
A. subopaca	✓	Epeolus cruciger	✓	Nomada argentata	✓		
A. synadelpha	✓	E. variegatus	✓	N. armata			
A. tarsata	✓	Eucera longicornis	✓	N. baccata	✓		
A. thoracica	✓	Halictus confusus	✓	N. fabriciana	✓		
A. tibialis	✓	H. rubicundus	✓	N. ferruginata	✓		
A. tridentata		H. tumulorum	✓	N. flava	✓		
A. trimmerana	✓	Heriades truncorum	✓	N. flavoguttata	✓		
A. varians	✓	Hoplitis claviventris	✓	N. flavopicta	✓		
A. wilkella	✓	Hylaeus brevicornis	✓	N. fucata	✓		
Anthidium manicatum	✓	H. communis	✓	N. fulvicornis	✓		
Anthophora bimaculata	✓	H. confusus	✓	N. goodeniana	✓		
A. furcata	✓	H. cornutus	✓	N. integra			
A. plumipes	✓	H. dilatatus	✓	N. lathburiana	✓		
A. quadrimaculata	✓	H. hyalinatus	✓	N. leucophthalma	✓		
A. retusa		H. pectoralis	✓	N. marshamella	✓		
Apis melllifera	✓	H. pictipes		N. obtusifrons			

Index

Scientific names are used throughout the book, common names are used only in the species accounts (page numbers in **bold**).

About the author

The author, Nick Owens, has had a passionate interest in wildlife since childhood. This led to a degree in Natural Sciences and PhD at Cambridge University. He then moved to Norfolk to study brent geese, beginning his love of Norfolk and its wildlife. A career change into teaching led him to Oundle School where he was Head of Science, returning to Norfolk for all family holidays. At Oundle he was active in practical conservation with pupils including work with the Northamptonshire Barn Owl Project. On retirement he happily returned to live in Norfolk where he developed his interest in bumblebees, leading to the publication of *Bumblebees of Norfolk* with the Norfolk and Norwich Naturalists Society and was Chairman of the NNNS from 2011–2014. From bumblebees came a growing interest in Norfolk's other bees and the publication of this book.

[GE]